Allen Carr became a qualified accountant in 1958. He was successful in his chosen profession, but his hundred-cigarettes-a-day addiction was driving him to despair. In 1983, after countless failed attempts to quit by using willpower and other methods, he finally discovered what the world had been waiting for – the Easy Way To Stop Smoking. Since leaving accountancy to help cure the world's smokers, Allen has built up a global reputation as a result of the phenomenal success of his method. He is now recognized as the world's leading expert on helping smokers to quit. Smokers used to have to fly from all over the world to attend his clinic in London; now his network of clinics spans the globe. *Allen Carr's Easy Way to Stop Smoking* is an international bestseller that has sold over one million copies and been published in over fifteen different languages.

ALLEN CARR'S

—

EASY WAY
TO
STOP
SMOKING

To all the smokers I have failed to cure.
I hope it will help them to get
free.

And to Sid Sutton.

But most of all to Joyce

This edition published for Prospero Books
a division of Chapters Inc.

This edition printed 1999

Copyright © Allen Carr 1985, 1991, 1997
All rights reserved

First published privately, under the title *The Easy Way To Stop Smoking*
in Great Britain by Allen Carr 1985

Copyright information held in Canada
By Chapters Inc.
90 Ronson Drive
Etobicoke, Ontario
M9W 1C1

Printed and bound in Finland

ISBN 0 88665 348 7

Contents

Preface

At last the miracle cure all smokers have been waiting for:

- ★ Instantaneous
- ★ Equally effective for the heavy smoker
- ★ No bad withdrawal pangs
- ★ Needs no willpower
- ★ No shock treatment
- ★ No aids or gimmicks required
- ★ You will not even put on weight
- ★ Permanent

If you are a smoker all you have to do is read on.

If you are a non-smoker purchasing for loved ones all you have to do is persuade them to read the book. If you cannot persuade them, then read the book yourself, and the last chapter will advise you how to get the message across – also how to prevent your children from starting. Do not be fooled by the fact that they hate it now. All children do before they become hooked.

Introduction

'I'M GOING TO CURE THE WORLD OF SMOKING.'
I was talking to my wife. She thought that I had flipped.
Understandable if you consider that she had watched me making a
really serious attempt to stop myself about every second year.
More understandable when you consider that the last attempt had
left me crying like a baby because I'd failed, yet again, after six
months of sheer purgatory. I was crying because I knew that if I
didn't succeed this time, I would be a smoker for life. I'd put so
much effort into the attempt that I knew I would never have the
strength to go through the ordeal again. Even more understandable when you consider that I made that statement having just
extinguished my final cigarette. Not only was I cured but I was
going to cure the rest of the world!

As I look back on my life, it seems that my whole existence has
been a preparation for solving the smoking problem. Even those
hateful years of training and practising as a chartered accountant
were invaluable in helping me to unravel the mysteries of the
smoking trap. They say you can't fool all the people all of the time,
but I believe that the tobacco companies have done just that for
years. I also believe I am the first to really understand the smoking
trap. If I appear to be arrogant, let me hasten to add that it was no
credit to me, just the circumstances of my life.

The momentous day was 15 July 1983. I didn't escape from
Colditz, but I imagine those who did felt the same relief that I felt
when I extinguished that last cigarette. I realized I had discovered
something that every smoker was praying for: an easy way to stop
smoking. After experimenting with friends and relatives I became
a full-time consultant, helping other smokers to get free.

I wrote the first edition of this book in 1985. One of my failures,
the man I describe in chapter 25, was the inspiration. He visited
me twice, and we were both reduced to tears on each occasion. He

was so agitated that I couldn't get him relaxed enough to understand what I was saying. I thought that if I wrote it all down, he could read it in his own good time, as many times as he wanted to, and this would help him to absorb the message.

I'm writing this introduction on the occasion of the publication of this edition of the book. I look at the front cover: there's a little red flash telling me it's been a bestseller every year. I think of all the thousands of letters I have received from smokers and their relatives all over the world thanking me for writing the book. Regrettably I don't have time to reply to all of those letters, but every one of them gives me pleasure, and just one such letter makes the whole thing worth while.

It never ceases to amaze me that every day I learn something new about smoking. Even so, the basic philosophy of the book remains sound. There may be no such thing as perfection, but the one chapter I would never change, the chapter I found easiest to write and, incidentally, most readers' favourite chapter, is chapter 21.

In addition to my own experience of consultation I also have the advantage of five years' feedback from the book itself. The alterations I have made to the first edition are to tune and refine the message, concentrating on the failures and trying to eradicate the reason for failure. Most of my failures are youngsters who have been forced to see me by their parents and who have no desire to stop. I even cure 75 per cent of those. Occasionally I get a genuine failure, someone who desperately wants to stop, like the man in chapter 25. It hurts me deeply, and at times I can't sleep for thinking how to get through to that smoker. I see the failure not as the smoker's but as mine because I've failed to make that smoker understand how easy it is to stop and how much more enjoyable life will be when he or she has escaped from the prison. I know that every smoker can find it not only easy but enjoyable to stop, but some people are so fixed in their views that they are incapable of using their imagination – the fear of stopping prevents them from opening their minds. It never occurs to them that cigarettes cause that fear and that the greatest gain they will receive in stopping is to be rid of that fear.

I dedicated the first edition to the 16 to 20 per cent of people whom I failed to cure. This was based on the money-back guarantee that I give at my consultations.

I have received many criticisms about my method over the years, but I know it will work for any smoker. The most frequent complaint I hear is 'Your method didn't work for me.' The smokers tell me that they acted in a way that was completely opposed to half my instructions – and then they can't understand why they are still smoking! Imagine spending your life wandering around a maze, unable to get out. I've got a plan of the maze, and I say to you, 'Take a left turn, then a right turn,' etc., etc. If you miss just one instruction, the rest of the instructions will be meaningless; you'll never escape the maze.

My original consultations were conducted on a one-to-one basis. I could persuade only desperate smokers to see me. I was regarded as some sort of quack. Now I'm regarded as the leading expert on stopping smoking, and people fly in from all over the world to see me. I treat groups of eight smokers at a time, and I still can't accommodate all the smokers who wish to see me, yet I don't advertise. If you look me up in the telephone directory, you'll see nothing about smoking.

At practically every session an ex-alcoholic or ex-heroin addict is present, or someone who has kicked the lot. I've been trying my method with alcoholics and heroin addicts and I've found that, provided they haven't attended AA or NA first, they are easier to cure than smokers. The method will work for all drug addiction.

I find the most disturbing factor of all is the ease with which ex-addicts get hooked again, whether they were smokers, heroin addicts or alcoholics. The most pathetic letters that I get are from smokers who have read this book, or quit with the help of my video, and have then got hooked again. They are so pleased to be free at first, but they fall into the pit again and find it doesn't work for them the next time. I am anxious to cover this problem, to help those smokers stop again and to explain the relationship between alcohol, other drugs and smoking, but I realize this is the subject for a whole new book. I'm working on it now.

By far the most common criticism is that the book is repetitive. I make no apology for this. As I explain in the book, the main problem is not the chemical addiction but the brainwashing that results from it. Ironically, it's the smokers who complain about the repetition who seem to fail. I wonder why?

As I've said, I receive a lot of praise and some criticism. In the early days I got some stick from the medical profession, but today it is my most ardent supporter. In fact, the nicest compliment I have received was from a doctor. He merely said, 'I wish I'd written that book.'

1

The Worst Nicotine Addict
I Have Yet to Meet

Perhaps I should begin by describing my competency for writing this book. No, I am not a doctor or a psychiatrist; my qualifications are far more appropriate. I spent thirty-three years of my life as a confirmed smoker. In the later years I smoked a hundred a day on a bad day, and never less than sixty.

During my life I had made dozens of attempts to stop. I once stopped for six months, and I was still climbing up the wall, still standing near smokers trying to get a whiff of the tobacco, still travelling in the smokers' compartments on trains.

With most smokers, on the health side, it's a question of 'I'll stop before it happens to me.' I had reached the stage where I knew it was killing me. I had a permanent headache with the pressure of the constant coughing. I could feel the continuous throbbing in the vein that runs vertically down the centre of my forehead, and I honestly believed that any moment there would be an explosion in my head and I would die from a brain haemorrhage. It bothered me, but it still didn't stop me.

I had reached the stage where I gave up even trying to stop. It was not so much that I enjoyed smoking. Some time in their lives most smokers have suffered from the illusion that they enjoy the odd cigarette, but I never suffered from that illusion. I have always detested the taste and smell, but I thought a cigarette helped me to relax. It gave me courage and confidence, and I was always miserable when I tried to stop, never being able to visualize an enjoyable life without a cigarette.

Eventually my wife sent me to a hypnotherapist. I must confess that I was completely sceptical, knowing nothing about hypnosis in those days and having visions of a Svengali-type figure with piercing eyes and waving pendula. I had all the normal illusions that smokers have about smoking except one – I knew that I wasn't a weak-willed person. With all other events in my life I was

1

in control. Cigarettes controlled me. I thought that hypnosis involved the forcing of wills, and although I was not obstructive (like most smokers, I dearly wanted to stop), I thought no one was going to kid me that I didn't need to smoke.

The whole session appeared to be a waste of time. The hypnotherapist tried to make me lift my arms and do various other things. Nothing appeared to be working properly. I didn't lose consciousness. I didn't go into a trance, or at least I didn't think I did, and yet after that session not only did I stop smoking but I actually enjoyed the process even during the withdrawal period.

Now, before you go rushing off to see a hypnotherapist, let me make something quite clear. Hypnotherapy is a means of communication. If the wrong message is communicated, you won't stop smoking. I'm loath to criticize the man whom I consulted because I would be dead by now if I hadn't seen him. But it was in spite of him, not because of him. Neither do I wish to appear to be knocking hypnotherapy; on the contrary, I use it as part of my own consultations. It is the power of suggestion and a powerful force that can be used for good or evil. Don't ever consult a hypnotherapist unless he or she has been personally recommended by someone you respect and trust.

During those awful years as a smoker I thought that my life depended on those cigarettes, and I was prepared to die rather than be without them. Today people ask me whether I ever have the odd pang. The answer is, 'Never, never, never' – just the reverse. I've had a marvellous life. If I had died through smoking, I couldn't have complained. I have been a very lucky man, but the most marvellous thing that has ever happened to me is being freed from that nightmare, that slavery of having to go through life systematically destroying your own body and paying through the nose for the privilege.

Let me make it quite clear from the beginning: I am not a mystical figure. I do not believe in magicians or fairies. I have a scientific brain, and I couldn't understand what appeared to me like magic. I started reading up on hypnosis and on smoking. Nothing I read seemed to explain the miracle that had happened. Why had it been so ridiculously easy to stop, whereas previously it had been weeks of black depression?

It took me a long time to work it all out, basically because I was going about it back to front. I was trying to work out why it had been so easy to stop, whereas the real problem is trying to explain why smokers find it *difficult* to stop. Smokers talk about the terrible withdrawal pangs, but when I looked back and tried to remember those awful pangs, they didn't exist for me. There was no physical pain. It was all in the mind.

My full-time profession is now helping other people to kick the habit. I'm very, very successful. I have helped to cure thousands of smokers. Let me emphasize from the start: there is no such thing as a confirmed smoker. I have still not met anybody who was as badly hooked (or, rather, *thought* he was as badly hooked) as myself. Anybody can not only stop smoking but find it easy to stop. It is basically fear that keeps us smoking, the fear that life will never be quite as enjoyable without cigarettes and the fear of feeling deprived. In fact, nothing could be further from the truth. Not only is life just as enjoyable without them but it is infinitely more so in many ways and that extra health, energy and wealth are the least of the advantages.

All smokers can find it easy to stop smoking – even you! All you have to do is read the rest of the book with an open mind. The more you can understand, the easier you will find it. Even if you do not understand a word, provided you follow the instructions you will find it easy. Most important of all, you will not go through life moping about cigarettes or feeling deprived. The only mystery will be why you did it for so long.

Let me issue a warning. There are only two reasons for failure with my method:

1 **FAILURE TO CARRY OUT INSTRUCTIONS** Some people find it annoying that I am so dogmatic about certain recommendations. For example, I will tell you not to try cutting down or using substitutes like sweets, chewing gum, etc. (particularly anything containing nicotine). The reason why I am so dogmatic is because I know my subject. I do not deny that there are many people who have succeeded in stopping using such ruses, but they have succeeded in spite of, not because of, them. There are people who can make love standing on a hammock, but it is not the easiest way. Everything I tell you has a purpose: to make it easy to stop and thereby ensure success.

2 **FAILURE TO UNDERSTAND** Do not take anything for granted. Question not only what I tell you but also your own views and what society has taught you about smoking. For example, those of you who think it is just a habit, ask

yourselves why other habits, some of them enjoyable ones, are easy to break, yet a habit that tastes awful, costs us a fortune and kills us is so difficult to break.

Those of you who think you enjoy a cigarette, ask yourselves why other things in life, which are infinitely more enjoyable, you can take or leave. Why do you *have* to have the cigarette and panic sets in if you don't?

2

The Easy Method

The object of this book is to get you into the frame of mind in which, instead of the normal method of stopping whereby you start off with the feeling that you are climbing Mount Everest and spend the next few weeks craving a cigarette and envying other smokers, you start right away with a feeling of elation, as if you had been cured of a terrible disease. From then on, the further you go through life the more you will look at cigarettes and wonder how you ever smoked them in the first place. You will look at smokers with pity as opposed to envy.

Provided that you are not a non-smoker or an ex-smoker, it is essential to keep smoking until you have finished the book completely. This may appear to be a contradiction. Later I shall be explaining that cigarettes do absolutely nothing for you at all. In fact, one of the many conundrums about smoking is that when we are actually smoking the cigarette, we look at it and wonder why we are doing it. It is only when we have been deprived that the cigarette becomes precious. However, let us accept that, whether you like it or not, you believe you are hooked. When you believe you are hooked, you can never be completely relaxed or concentrate properly unless you are smoking. So do not attempt to stop smoking before you have finished the whole book. As you read further your desire to smoke will gradually be reduced. Do not go off half-cocked; this could be fatal. Remember, all you have to do is to follow the instructions.

With the benefit of five years' feedback since the book's original publication, apart from chapter 28, 'Timing', this instruction to continue to smoke until you have completed the book has caused me more frustration than any other. When I first stopped smoking, many of my relatives and friends stopped, purely because I had done it. They thought, 'If he can do it, anybody can.' Over the years, by dropping little hints I managed to persuade the ones that hadn't stopped to realize just how nice it is to be free! When the book was first printed I gave copies to the hard core who were still puffing away. I worked on the basis that, even if it were the most boring book ever written, they would still read it, if only because it had been written by a friend. I was surprised and hurt to learn that, months later, they hadn't bothered to finish the book. I even discovered that the original copy I had signed and given to someone who was then my closest friend had not only been ignored but actually given away. I was hurt at the time, but I had overlooked the dreadful fear that slavery to the weed instils in the smoker. It can transcend friendship. I nearly provoked a divorce because of it. My mother once said to my wife, 'Why don't you threaten to leave him if he doesn't stop smoking?' My wife said, 'Because he'd leave me if I did.' I'm ashamed to admit it, but I believe she was right, such is the fear that smoking creates. I now realize that many smokers don't finish the book because they feel they have got to stop smoking when they do. Some deliberately read only one line a day in order to postpone the evil day. Now I am fully aware that many readers are having their arms twisted, by people that love them, to read the book. Look at it this way: what have you got to lose? If you don't stop at the end of the book, you are no worse off than you are now. YOU HAVE ABSOLUTELY NOTHING TO LOSE AND SO MUCH TO GAIN! Incidentally, if you have not smoked for a few days or weeks but are not sure whether you are a smoker, an ex-smoker or a non-smoker, then don't smoke while you read. In fact, you are already a non-smoker. All we've now got to do is to let your brain catch up with your body. By the end of the book you'll be a happy non-smoker.

Basically my method is the complete opposite of the normal method of trying to stop. The *normal* method is to list the considerable disadvantages of smoking and say, 'If only I can go long enough without a cigarette, eventually the desire to smoke will go. I can then enjoy life again, free of slavery to the weed.'

This is the logical way to go about it, and thousands of smokers are stopping every day using variations of this method. However, it is very difficult to succeed using this method for the following reasons:

1 Stopping smoking is not the real problem. Every time you put a cigarette out you stop smoking. You may have powerful reasons on day one to say, 'I do not want to smoke any more' – all smokers have, every day of their lives, and the reasons are

6

more powerful than you can possibly imagine. The real problem is day two, day ten or day ten thousand, when in a weak moment, an inebriated moment or even a strong moment you have one cigarette, and because it is partly drug addiction you then want another, and suddenly you are a smoker again.

2 The health scares should stop us. Our rational minds say, 'Stop doing it. You are a fool,' but in fact they make it harder. We smoke, for example, when we are nervous. Tell smokers that it is killing them, and the first thing they will do is to light a cigarette. There are more dogends outside the Royal Marsden Hospital, the country's foremost cancer treatment establishment, than any other hospital in the country.

3 All reasons for stopping actually make it harder for two other reasons. *First*, they create a sense of sacrifice. We are always being forced to give up our little friend or prop or vice or pleasure, whichever way the smoker sees it. *Secondly*, they create a 'blind'. We do not smoke for the reasons we should stop. The real question is 'Why do we want or need to do it?'

The Easy Method is basically this: initially to forget the reasons we'd like to stop, to face the cigarette problem and to ask ourselves the following questions:

1 What is it doing for me?
2 Do I actually enjoy it?
3 Do I really need to go through life paying through the nose just to stick these things in my mouth and suffocate myself?

The beautiful truth is that it does absolutely nothing for you at all. Let me make it quite clear, I do not mean that the disadvantages of being a smoker outweigh the advantages; all smokers know that all their lives. I mean there are not *any* advantages from smoking. The only advantage it ever had was the social 'plus'; nowadays even smokers themselves regard it as an antisocial habit.

Most smokers find it necessary to rationalize why they smoke, but the reasons are all fallacies and illusions.

The first thing we are going to do is to remove these fallacies and illusions. In fact, you will realize that there is nothing to give up. Not only is there nothing to give up but there are marvellous, positive gains from being a non-smoker, and health and money are only two of these gains. Once the illusion that life will never be quite as enjoyable without the cigarette is removed, once you realize that not only is life just as enjoyable without it but infinitely more so, once the feeling of being deprived or of missing out are eradicated, then we can go back to the health and money – and the dozens of other reasons for stopping smoking. These realizations will become positive additional aids to help you achieve what you really desire – to enjoy the whole of your life free from the slavery of the weed.

3

Why is it Difficult to Stop?

As I explained earlier, I got interested in this subject because of my own addiction. When I finally stopped it was like magic. When I had previously tried to stop there were weeks of black depression. There would be odd days when I was comparatively cheerful but the next day back with the depression. It was like clawing your way out of a slippery pit, you feel you are near the top, you see the sunshine and then find yourself sliding down again. Eventually you light that cigarette, it tastes awful and you try to work out why you have to do it.

One of the questions I always ask smokers prior to my consultations is 'Do you want to stop smoking?' In a way it is a stupid question. All smokers (including members of FOREST) would love to stop smoking. If you say to the most confirmed smoker, 'If you could go back to the time before you became hooked, with the knowledge you have now, would you have started smoking?', 'NO WAY' is the reply.

Say to the most confirmed smoker – someone who doesn't think that it injures his health, who is not worried about the social stigma and who can afford it (there are not many about these days) – 'Do you encourage your children to smoke?' 'NO WAY' is the reply.

All smokers feel that something evil has got possession of them. In the early days it is a question of 'I am going to stop, not today but tomorrow.' Eventually we get to the stage where we think either that we haven't got the willpower or that there is something inherent in the cigarette that we must have in order to enjoy life.

As I said previously, the problem is not explaining why it is easy to stop; *it is explaining why it is difficult.* In fact, the real problem is explaining why anybody does it in the first place or why, at one time, over 60 per cent of the population were smoking.

The whole business of smoking is an extraordinary enigma. The

9

only reason we get on to it is because of the thousands of people already doing it. Yet every one of them wishes he or she had not started in the first place, telling us that it is a waste of time and money. We cannot quite believe they are not enjoying it. We associate it with being grown up and work hard to become hooked ourselves. We then spend the rest of our lives telling our own children not to do it and trying to kick the habit ourselves.

We also spend the rest of our lives paying through the nose. The average twenty-a-day smoker spends $60,000 in his/her lifetime on cigarettes. What do we do with that money? (It wouldn't be so bad if we threw it down the drain.) We actually use it systematically to congest our lungs with cancerous tars, progressively to clutter up and poison our blood vessels. Each day we are increasingly starving every muscle and organ of our bodies of oxygen, so that each day we become more lethargic. We sentence ourselves to a lifetime of filth, bad breath, stained teeth, burnt clothes, filthy ashtrays and the foul smell of stale tobacco. It is a lifetime of slavery. We spend half our lives in situations in which society forbids us to smoke (churches, hospitals, schools, Tube trains, theatres, etc.) or, when we are trying to cut down or stop, feeling deprived. The rest of our smoking lives is spent in situations where we are allowed to smoke but wish we didn't have to. What sort of hobby is it that when you are doing it you wish you weren't, and when you are not doing it you crave a cigarette? It's a lifetime of being treated by half of society like some sort of leper and, worst of all, a lifetime of an otherwise intelligent, rational human being going through life in contempt. The smoker despises himself, every Budget Day, every National Non-Smoking Day, every time he inadvertently reads the government health warning or there is a cancer scare or a bad-breath campaign, every time he gets congested or has a pain in the chest, every time he is the lone smoker in company with non-smokers. Having to go through life with these awful black shadows at the back of his mind, what does he get out of it? ABSOLUTELY NOTHING! Pleasure? Enjoyment? Relaxation? A prop? A boost? All illusions, unless you consider the wearing of tight shoes to enjoy the removal of them as some sort of pleasure!

As I have said, the real problem is trying to explain not only why smokers find it difficult to stop but why anybody does it at all.

You are probably saying, 'That's all very well. I know this, but once you are hooked on these things it is very difficult to stop.' But why is it so difficult, and why do we have to do it? Smokers search for the answer to these questions all of their lives.

Some say it is because of the powerful withdrawal symptoms. In fact, the actual withdrawal symptoms from nicotine are so mild (see chapter 6) that most smokers have lived and died without ever realizing they are drug addicts.

Some say cigarettes are very enjoyable. They aren't. They are filthy, disgusting objects. Ask any smoker who thinks he smokes only because he enjoys a cigarette if, when he hasn't got his own brand and can only obtain a brand he finds distasteful, he stops smoking? Smokers would rather smoke old rope than not smoke at all. Enjoyment has nothing to do with it. I enjoy lobster but I never got to the stage where I had to have twenty lobsters hanging round my neck. With other things in life we enjoy them whilst we are doing them but we don't sit feeling deprived when we are not.

Some search for deep psychological reasons, the 'Freud syndrome', 'the child at the mother's breast'. Really it is just the reverse. The usual reason why we start smoking is to show we are grown up and mature. If we had to suck a dummy in company, we would die of embarrassment.

Some think it is the reverse, the macho effect of breathing smoke or fire down your nostrils. Again this argument has no substance. A burning cigarette in the ear would appear ridiculous. How much more ridiculous to breathe cancer-triggering tars into your lungs.

Some say, 'It is something to do with my hands!' So, why light it?

'It is oral satisfaction.' So, why light it?

'It is the feeling of the smoke going into my lungs.' An awful feeling – it is called suffocation.

Many believe smoking relieves boredom. This is also a fallacy. Boredom is a frame of mind.

For thirty-three years my reason was that it relaxed me, gave me confidence and courage. I also knew it was killing me and costing me a fortune. Why didn't I go to my doctor and ask him for an alternative to relax me and give me courage and confidence? I didn't go because I knew he would suggest an alternative. It wasn't my reason; it was my excuse.

Some say they only do it because their friends do it. Are you really that stupid? If so, just pray that your friends do not start cutting their heads off to cure a headache!

Most smokers who think about it eventually come to the conclusion that it is just a habit. This is not really an explanation but, having discounted all the usual rational explanations, it appears

11

to be the only remaining excuse. Unfortunately, this explanation is equally illogical. Every day of our lives we change habits, and some of them are very enjoyable. My eating habits relate back to my smoking days. I do not eat breakfast or lunch; I have just one meal a day, in the evening. Yet when I go on holiday my favourite meal is breakfast. The day I return I revert to my normal habit without the slightest effort.

Why do we pursue a habit that tastes awful, that kills us, that costs us a fortune, that is filthy and disgusting and that we would dearly love to break anyway, when all we have to do is to stop doing it? Why is it so difficult? The answer is, it isn't. It is ridiculously easy. Once you understand the real reasons why you smoke, you will stop doing it – just like that – and in three weeks' time at the most the only mystery will be why you smoked so long in the first place.

READ ON.

4

The Sinister Trap

Smoking is the most subtle, sinister trap in nature. Man could not begin to conceive of anything so ingenious. What gets us into it in the first place? The thousands of adults who are already doing it. They even warn us that it's a filthy, disgusting habit that will eventually destroy us and will keep us poor for the rest of our lives, but we cannot believe that they are not enjoying it. One of the many pathetic aspects of the smoking habit is how hard we have to work in order to become hooked.

It is the only trap in nature which has no lure, no piece of cheese. The thing that springs the trap is not that cigarettes taste so marvellous; it's that they taste so awful. If that first cigarette tasted marvellous, alarm bells would ring and, as intelligent human beings, we could then understand why half the adult population was systematically paying through the nose to poison itself. But because that first cigarette tastes awful, our young minds are reassured that we will never become hooked, and we think that because we are not enjoying them we can stop whenever we want to.

It is the only drug in nature that prevents you from achieving your aim. Boys usually start because they want to appear tough – it is the Humphrey Bogart/Clint Eastwood image. The last thing you feel with the first cigarette is tough. You dare not inhale, and if you have too many, you start to feel dizzy, then sick. All you want to do is get away from the other boys and throw the filthy things away.

With women, the aim is to be the sophisticated modern young lady. We have all seen them taking little puffs on a cigarette, looking absolutely ridiculous. By the time the boys have learnt to look tough and the girls have learnt to look sophisticated, they wish they had never started in the first place.

We then spend the rest of our lives trying to explain to ourselves why we do it, telling our children not to get caught and, at odd times, trying to escape ourselves.

The trap is so designed that we try to stop only when we have stress in our lives, whether it be health, shortage of money or just plain being made to feel like a leper.

As soon as we stop, we have more stress (the fearful withdrawal pangs of nicotine) and the thing that we rely on to relieve stress (our old prop, the cigarette) we now must do without.

After a few days of torture we decide that we have picked the wrong time. We must wait for a period without stress, and as soon as that arrives the reason for stopping vanishes. Of course, that period will never arrive because, in the first place, we think that our lives tend to become more and more stressful. As we leave the protection of our parents, the natural process is setting up home, mortgages, babies, more responsible jobs, etc., etc. This is also an illusion. The truth is that the most stressful periods for any creature are early childhood and adolescence. We tend to confuse responsibility with stress. Smokers' lives automatically become more stressful because tobacco does not relax you or relieve stress, as society tries to make you believe. Just the reverse: it actually causes you to become more nervous and distressed.

Even those smokers who kick the habit (most do, one or more times during their lives) can lead perfectly happy lives yet suddenly become hooked again.

The whole business of smoking is like wandering into a giant maze. As soon as we enter the maze our minds become misted and clouded, and we spend the rest of our lives trying to escape. Many of us eventually do, only to find that we get trapped again at a later date.

I spent thirty-three years trying to escape from that maze. Like all smokers, I couldn't understand it. However, due to a combination of unusual circumstances, none of which reflect any credit on me, I wanted to know why it had been so desperately difficult to stop and yet, when I finally did, it was not only easy but enjoyable.

Since stopping smoking my hobby and, later, my profession has been to resolve the many conundrums associated with smoking. It is a complex and fascinating puzzle and, like the Rubik Cube, practically impossible to solve. However, like all complicated puzzles, if you know the solution, it is easy! I have the solution to stopping smoking easily. I will lead you out of the maze and ensure that you never wander into it again. All you have to do is *follow the instructions*. If you take a wrong turn, the rest of the instructions will be pointless.

Let me emphasize that anybody can find it easy to stop smoking, but first we need to establish the facts. No, I do not mean the scare facts. I know you are already aware of them. There is already enough information on the evils of smoking. If that was going to stop you, you would already have stopped. I mean, why do we find it difficult to stop? In order to answer this question we need to know the real reason why we are still smoking.

5

Why Do We Carry on Smoking?

We all start smoking for stupid reasons, usually social pressures or social occasions, but, once we feel we are becoming hooked, why do we carry on smoking?

No regular smoker knows why he or she smokes. If smokers knew the true reason, they would stop doing it. I have asked the question of thousands of smokers during my consultations. The true answer is the same for all smokers, but the variety of replies is infinite. I find this part of the consultation the most amusing and at the same time the most pathetic.

All smokers know in their heart of hearts that they are mugs. They know that they had no need to smoke before they became hooked. Most of them can remember that their first cigarette tasted awful and that they had to work hard in order to become hooked. The most annoying part is that they sense that non-smokers are not missing anything and that they are laughing at them (it is difficult not to on Budget Day).

However, smokers are intelligent, rational human beings. They know that they are taking enormous health risks and that they spend a fortune on cigarettes in their lifetime. Therefore it is necessary for them to have a rational explanation to justify their habit.

The actual reason why smokers continue to smoke is a subtle combination of the factors that I will elaborate in the next two chapters. They are:

1 NICOTINE ADDICTION
2 BRAINWASHING.

6

Nicotine Addiction

Nicotine, a colourless, oily compound, is the drug contained in tobacco that addicts the smoker. It is the fastest addictive drug known to mankind, and it can take just one cigarette to become hooked.

Every puff on a cigarette delivers, via the lungs to the brain, a small dose of nicotine that acts more rapidly than the dose of heroin the addict injects into his veins.

If there are twenty puffs for you in a cigarette, you receive twenty doses of the drug with just one cigarette.

Nicotine is a quick-acting drug, and levels in the bloodstream fall quickly to about half within thirty minutes of smoking a cigarette and to a quarter within an hour of finishing a cigarette. This explains why most smokers average about twenty per day.

As soon as the smoker extinguishes the cigarette, the nicotine rapidly starts to leave the body and the smoker begins to suffer withdrawal pangs.

I must at this point dispel a common illusion that smokers have about withdrawal pangs. Smokers think that withdrawal pangs are the terrible trauma they suffer when they try or are forced to stop smoking. They are, in fact, mainly mental; the smoker is feeling deprived of his pleasure or prop. I will explain more about this later.

The actual pangs of withdrawal from nicotine are so subtle that most smokers have lived and died without even realizing they are drug addicts. When we use the term 'nicotine addicts' we think we just 'got into the habit'. Most smokers have a horror of drugs, yet that's exactly what they are – drug addicts. Fortunately it is an easy drug to kick, but you need first to accept that you are addicted.

There is no physical pain in the withdrawal from nicotine. It is merely an empty, restless feeling, the feeling of something missing, which is why many smokers think it is something to do with hands. If it is prolonged, the smoker becomes nervous, insecure, agitated, lacking in confidence and irritable. It is like hunger – for a poison, NICOTINE.

Within seven seconds of lighting a cigarette fresh nicotine is supplied and the craving ends, resulting in the feeling of relaxation and confidence that the cigarette gives to the smoker.

In the early days, when we first start smoking, the withdrawal pangs and their relief are so slight that we are not even aware that they exist. When we begin to smoke regularly we think it is because we've either come to enjoy them or got into the 'habit'. The truth is we're already hooked; we do not realize it, but that little nicotine monster is already inside our stomach and every now and again we have to feed it.

All smokers start smoking for stupid reasons. Nobody has to. The only reason why anybody continues smoking, whether they be a casual or a heavy smoker, is to feed that little monster.

The whole business of smoking is a series of conundrums. All smokers know at heart that they are mugs and have been trapped by something evil. However, I think the most pathetic aspect about smoking is that the enjoyment that the smoker gets from a cigarette is the pleasure of trying to get back to the state of peace, tranquillity and confidence that his body had before he became hooked in the first place.

You know that feeling when a neighbour's burglar alarm has been ringing all day, or there has been some other minor, persistent aggravation. Then the noise suddenly stops – that marvellous feeling of peace and tranquillity is experienced. It is not really peace but the ending of the aggravation.

Before we start the nicotine chain, our bodies are complete. We then force nicotine into the body, and when we put that cigarette out and the nicotine starts to leave, we suffer withdrawal pangs – not physical pain, just an empty feeling. We are not even aware that it exists, but it is like a dripping tap inside our bodies. Our rational minds do not understand it. They do not need to. All we know is that we want a cigarette, and when we light it the craving goes, and for the moment we are content and confident again just as we were before we became addicted. However, the satisfaction is only temporary because, in order to relieve the craving, you have to put more nicotine into the body. As soon as you extinguish that cigarette the craving starts again, and so the chain goes on. It is a chain for life – UNLESS YOU BREAK IT.

18

The whole business of smoking is like wearing tight shoes just to obtain the pleasure you feel when you take them off. There are three main reasons why smokers cannot see things that way.

1 There is no physical pain that we can identify. It is just a feeling.
2 It happens in reverse. This is why all drugs are difficult to kick. It is when you are not smoking that you suffer the feeling – you do not blame the cigarette. When you light up you obtain relief – so you are fooled into believing the cigarette is some sort of pleasure or prop.
3 The massive brainwashing that we have been subjected to since birth. Although our lives were complete before we started smoking, it comes as no surprise to learn that, once we get over the learning process, cigarettes do provide a crutch or pleasure. Why should we even question it? We are now among the 'happy' band of smokers.

It may be as well to dispel some of the illusions about smoking at this point. The 'habit' doesn't exist. We have all sorts of habits during life, some of them very enjoyable. With a habit that tastes awful, kills us, costs us a fortune, that we regard as filthy and disgusting and that we would like to be free of anyway, it should be ridiculously easy to break. Why do we find it so difficult? The answer is that it is not habit but drug addiction. We have to force ourselves to learn to cope with it. Before we know it, we are not only buying them regularly but we *have* to have them. If we don't, panic sets in, and as we go through life we tend to smoke more and more.

This is because, as with any other drug, the body tends to become immune to the effects of nicotine and our intake tends to increase. After quite a short period of smoking the cigarette ceases to relieve completely the withdrawal pangs that it creates, so that when you light up a cigarette you feel better than you did a moment before, but you are in fact more nervous and less relaxed than you would be as a non-smoker, even when you are actually smoking the cigarette. The practice is even more ridiculous than wearing tight shoes because as you go through life an increasing amount of the pain remains even when the shoes are removed.

The position is even worse because, once the cigarette is extinguished, the nicotine rapidly begins to leave the body, which explains why, in stress situations, the smoker tends to chain smoke.

As I said, the 'habit' doesn't exist. The real reason why every smoker goes on smoking is because of that little monster inside his stomach. Every now and again he has to feed it. The smoker himself will decide when he does that, and it tends to be on four types of occasion or a combination of them.

They are:

BOREDOM/CONCENTRATION – two complete opposites!
STRESS/RELAXATION – two complete opposites!

What magic drug can suddenly reverse the very effect it had twenty minutes before? If you think about it, what other types of occasion are there in our lives, apart from sleep? The truth is that smoking neither relieves boredom and stress nor promotes concentration and relaxation. It is all just illusion.

Apart from being a drug, nicotine is also a powerful poison and is used in insecticides (look it up in your dictionary). The nicotine content of just one cigarette, if injected directly into a vein, would kill you. In fact, tobacco contains many poisons, including carbon monoxide.

In case you have visions of switching to a pipe or to cigars, I should make it quite clear that the content of this book applies to all tobacco.

The human body is the most sophisticated object on our planet. No species, even the lowest amoeba or worm, can survive without knowing the difference between food and poison.

Through a process of natural selection over thousands of years, our minds and bodies have developed techniques for distinguishing between food and poison and fail-safe methods for ejecting the latter.

All human beings are averse to the smell and taste of tobacco until they become hooked. If you blow diluted tobacco into the face of any animal or child before it becomes hooked, it will cough and splutter.

When we smoked that first cigarette, inhaling resulted in a coughing fit, or if we smoked too many the first time, we experienced a dizzy feeling or actual physical sickness. It was our body telling us, 'YOU ARE FEEDING ME POISON. STOP DOING IT.' This is the stage that often decides whether we become smokers or not. It is a fallacy that physically weak and mentally weak-willed people become smokers. The lucky ones are those who find that first cigarette repulsive; physically their lungs cannot cope with it, and they are cured for life. Or, alternatively, they are not mentally prepared to go through the severe learning process of trying to inhale without coughing.

To me this is the most tragic part of this whole business. How hard we worked to become hooked, and this is why it is difficult to stop teenagers. Because they are still learning to smoke, because they still find cigarettes distasteful, they believe they can stop whenever they want to. Why do they not learn from us? Then again, why did we not learn from our parents?

Many smokers believe they enjoy the taste and smell of the tobacco. It is an illusion. What we are actually doing when we learn to smoke is teaching our bodies to become immune to the bad smell and taste in order to get our fix, like heroin addicts who think that they enjoy injecting themselves. The withdrawal pangs from heroin are very severe, and all they are really enjoying is the ritual of relieving those pangs.

The smoker teaches himself to shut his mind to the bad taste and smell to get his 'fix'. Ask a smoker who believes he smokes only because he enjoys the taste and smell of tobacco, 'If you cannot get your normal brand of cigarette and can only obtain a brand you find distasteful, do you stop smoking?' No way. A smoker will smoke old rope rather than abstain, and it doesn't matter if you switch to roll-ups, mentholated cigarettes, cigars or a pipe; to begin with they taste awful but if you persevere you will learn to like them. Smokers will even try to keep smoking during colds, 'flu, sore throats, bronchitis and emphysema.

Enjoyment has nothing to do with it. If it did, no one would smoke more than one cigarette. There are even thousands of ex-smokers hooked on that filthy nicotine chewing gum that doctors prescribe, and many of them are still smoking.

During my consultations some smokers find it alarming to realize they are drug addicts and think it will make it even more difficult to stop. In fact, it is all good news for two important reasons.

1 The reason why most of us carry on smoking is because, although we know the disadvantages outweigh the advantages, we believe that there is something in the cigarette that we actually enjoy or that it is some sort of prop. We feel that after we stop smoking there will be a void, that certain

21

situations in our life will never be quite the same. This is an illusion. The fact is the cigarette gives nothing; it only takes away and then partially restores to create the illusion. I will explain this in more detail in a later chapter.

2 Although it is the world's most powerful drug because of the speed with which you become hooked, you are never badly hooked. Because it is a quick-acting drug it takes only three weeks for 99 per cent of the nicotine to leave your body, and the actual withdrawal pangs are so mild that most smokers have lived and died without ever realizing that they have suffered them.

You will quite rightly ask why it is that many smokers find it so difficult to stop, go through months of torture and spend the rest of their lives pining for a cigarette at odd times? The answer is the second reason why we smoke – the Brainwashing. The chemical addiction is easy to cope with.

Most smokers go all night without a cigarette. The withdrawal pangs do not even wake them up.

Many smokers will actually leave the bedroom before they light that first cigarette; many will have breakfast first; many will wait until they arrive at work. They can suffer ten hours' withdrawal pangs, and it doesn't bother them, but if they went ten hours during the day without a cigarette, they'd be tearing their hair out.

Many smokers will buy a new car nowadays and refrain from smoking in it. Many will visit theatres, supermarkets, churches, etc., and not being able to smoke doesn't bother them. Even on the Tube trains there have been no riots. Smokers are almost pleased for someone or something to force them to stop smoking.

Nowadays many smokers will automatically refrain from smoking in the home of, or merely in the company of, non-smokers with little discomfort to themselves. In fact, most smokers have extended periods during which they abstain without effort. Even in my case I would quite happily relax all evening without a cigarette. In the later years as a smoker I actually used to look forward to the evenings when I could stop choking myself (what a ridiculous habit).

The chemical addiction is easy to cope with, even when you are still addicted, and there are thousands of smokers who remain casual smokers all their lives. They are just as heavily addicted as the heavy smoker. There are even heavy smokers who have kicked

22

the habit but will have an occasional cigar, and that keeps them addicted.

As I say, the actual nicotine addiction is not the main problem. It just acts like a catalyst to keep our minds confused over the real problem. The brainwashing.

It may be of consolation to lifelong and heavy smokers to know that it is just as easy for them to stop as casual smokers. In a peculiar way, it is easier. The further you go along with the habit, the more it drags you down and the greater the gain when you stop.

It may be of further consolation for you to know that the rumours that occasionally circulate (e.g. 'It takes seven years for the "gunge" to leave your body' or 'Every cigarette you smoke takes five minutes off your life') are untrue.

Do not think the bad effects of smoking are exaggerated. If anything, they are sadly understated, but the truth is the 'five minutes' rule is obviously an estimation and applies only if you contract one of the killer diseases or just 'gunge' yourself to a standstill.

In fact, the 'gunge' never leaves your body completely. If there are smokers about, it is in the atmosphere, and even non-smokers acquire a small percentage. However, these bodies of ours are incredible machines and have enormous powers of recovery, providing you haven't already triggered off one of the irreversible diseases. If you stop now, your body will recover within a matter of a few weeks, almost as if you had never been a smoker.

As I have said, it is never too late to stop. I have helped to cure many smokers in their fifties and sixties and even a few in their seventies and eighties. Recently a 91-year-old woman attended my clinic with her 65-year-old son. When I asked her why she had decided to stop smoking, she replied, 'To set an example for him.'

The further it drags you down, the greater the relief. When I finally stopped I went straight from a hundred a day to ZERO, and didn't have one bad pang. In fact, it was actually enjoyable, even during the withdrawal period.

But we *must* remove the brainwashing.

7

Brainwashing and the Sleeping Partner

How or why do we start smoking in the first place? To understand this fully you need to examine the powerful effect of the subconscious mind or, as I call it, the 'sleeping partner'.

We all tend to think we are intelligent, dominant human beings determining our paths through life. In fact, 99 per cent of our make-up is moulded. We are a product of the society that we are brought up in – the sort of clothes we wear, the houses we live in, our basic life patterns, even those matters on which we tend to differ, e.g. politics or religion. The subconscious is an extremely powerful influence in our lives, and even in matters of fact rather than opinion millions of people can be deluded. Before Columbus sailed round the world the majority of people knew it to be flat. Today we know it is round. If I wrote a dozen books trying to persuade you that it was flat, I could not do it, yet how many of us have been into space to see the ball? Even if you have flown or sailed round the world, how do you know that you were not travelling in a circle above a flat suface?

Advertising men know well the power of suggestion over the subconcious mind, hence the large posters the smoker is hit with as he drives around, the adverts in every magazine. You think they are a waste of money? That they do not persuade you to buy cigarettes? You are wrong! Try it out for yourself. Next time you go into a pub or restaurant on a cold day and your companion asks you what you are having to drink, instead of saying, 'A brandy' (or whatever), embellish it with 'Do you know what I would really enjoy today? That marvellous warm glow of a brandy.' You will find that even people who dislike brandy will join you.

From our earliest years our subconscious minds are bombarded daily with information telling us that cigarettes relax us and give us confidence and courage and that the most precious thing on

24

this earth is a cigarette. You think I exaggerate? Whenever you see a cartoon or film or play in which people are about to be executed or shot, what is their last request? That's right, a cigarette. The impact of this does not register on our conscious minds, but the sleeping partner has time to absorb it. What the message is really saying is, 'The most precious thing on this earth, my last thought and action, will be the smoking of a cigarette.' In every war film the injured man is given a cigarette.

You think that things have changed recently? No, our children are still being bombarded by large hoardings and magazine adverts. Cigarette advertising is supposed to be banned on television nowadays, yet during peak viewing hours the world's top snooker players and darts players are seen constantly puffing away. The programmes are usually sponsored by the tobacco giants, and this is the most sinister trend of all in today's advertising: the link with sporting occasions and the jet set. Grand Prix racing cars modelled and even named after cigarette brand names – or is it the other way round? There are even plugs on television nowadays depicting a naked couple sharing a cigarette in bed after having sex. The implications are obvious. How my admiration goes out to the advertisers of the small cigar, not for their motives but for the brilliance of their campaign, whereby a man is about to face death or disaster – his balloon is on fire and about to crash, or the sidecar of his motorbike is about to crash into a river, or he is Columbus and his ship is about to go over the edge of the world. Not a word is spoken. Soft music plays. He lights up a cigar; a look of sheer bliss covers his face. The conscious mind may not realize that the smoker is even watching the advert, but the 'sleeping partner' is patiently digesting the obvious implications.

True, there is publicity the other way – the cancer scares, the legs being amputated, the bad-breath campaigns – but these do not actually stop people smoking. Logically they should, but the fact is they do not. They do not even prevent youngsters from starting. All the years that I remained a smoker I honestly believed that, had I known of the links between lung cancer and cigarette smoking, I would never have become a smoker. The truth is that it doesn't make the slightest bit of difference. The trap is the same today as when Sir Walter Raleigh fell into it. All the anti-smoking campaigns just help to add to the confusion. Even the products themselves, those lovely shining packets that lure you to engulf their contents, contain a deadly warning on their sides. What smoker ever reads it, let alone brings himself to face the implications of it?

25

I believe that a leading cigarette manufacturer is actually using the Government Health Warning to sell its products. Many of the scenes include frightening features such as spiders, dragonflies and the Venus flytrap. The health warning is now so large and bold that the smoker cannot avoid it, however hard he tries. The pang of fear that the smoker suffers prompts an association of ideas with the glossy gold packet.

Ironically, the most powerful force in this brainwashing is the smoker himself. It is a fallacy that smokers are weak-willed and physically weak specimens. You have to be physically strong in order to cope with the poison.

This is one of the reasons why smokers refuse to accept the overwhelming statistics that prove that smoking cripples your health. Everyone knows of an Uncle Fred who smoked forty a day, never had a day's illness in his life, and lived to eighty. They refuse even to consider the hundreds of other smokers who are cut down in their prime or the fact that Uncle Fred might still be alive if he hadn't been a smoker.

If you do a small survey among your friends and colleagues, you will find that most smokers are, in fact, strong-willed people. They tend to be self-employed, business executives or in certain specialized professions, such as doctors, lawyers, policemen, teachers, salesmen, nurses, secretaries, housewives with children, etc. – in other words, anybody leading a stressful existence. The main delusion of smokers is that smoking relieves stress and tends to be associated with the dominant type, the type that takes on responsibility and stress, and, of course, that is the type that we admire and therefore tend to copy. Another group that tends to get hooked are people in monotonous jobs because the other main reason for smoking is boredom. Also an illusion, I am afraid.

The extent of the brainwashing is quite incredible. As a society we get all uptight about glue-sniffing, heroin addiction, etc. Actual deaths from glue-sniffing do not amount to ten per annum, and deaths from heroin are less than a hundred a year in this country.

There is another drug, nicotine, on which over 60 per cent of us become hooked at some time in our lives and the majority spend the rest of their lives paying through the nose. Most of their spare money goes on cigarettes and hundreds of thousands of people have their lives ruined every year because they became hooked. It is the No. 1 killer in western society, including road accidents, fires, etc.

Why is it that we regard glue-sniffing and heroin addiction as such great evils, while the drug that we spend most of our money on and is actually killing us we used to regard a few years ago as a perfectly acceptable social habit? In recent years it has been considered a slightly unsociable habit that may injure our health but is legal and on sale in glossy packets in every newsagent's, pub, club, garage and restaurant. The biggest vested interest is our own government. It makes billions per year out of smokers, and the tobacco companies spend hundreds of millions per year in promotion alone.

You need to start building resistance to this brainwashing, just as if you were buying a car from a secondhand dealer. You would be nodding politely but you would not believe a word the man was saying.

Start looking behind these glossy packets at the filth and poison beneath. Do not be fooled by the cut glass ashtrays or the gold lighter or the millions who have been conned. Start asking yourself:

Why am I doing it?

Do I really need to?

NO, OF COURSE YOU DON'T.

I find this brainwashing aspect the most difficult of all to explain. Why is it that an otherwise rational, intelligent human being becomes a complete imbecile about his own addiction? It pains me to confess that out of the thousands of people that I have assisted in kicking the habit, I was the biggest idiot of all.

Not only did I reach a hundred a day myself but my father was a heavy smoker. He was a strong man, cut down in his prime due to smoking. I can remember watching him when I was a boy; he would be coughing and spluttering in the mornings. I could see he wasn't enjoying it and it was so obvious to me that something evil had got possession of him. I can remember saying to my mother, 'Don't ever let me become a smoker.'

At the age of fifteen I was a physical-fitness fanatic. Sport was my life and I was full of courage and confidence. If anybody had said to me in those days that I would end up smoking a hundred cigarettes a day, I would have gambled my lifetime's earnings that it would not happen, and I would have given any odds that had been asked.

At the age of forty I was a physical and mental cigarette junky. I had reached the stage where I couldn't carry out the most mundane physical or mental act without first lighting up. With most smokers the triggers are the normal stresses of life, like answering the telephone or socializing. I couldn't even change a television programme or a light bulb without lighting up.

I knew it was killing me. There was no way I could kid myself otherwise. But why I couldn't see what it was doing to me mentally I cannot understand. It was almost jumping up and biting me on the nose. The ridiculous thing is that most smokers suffer the delusion at some time in their life that they enjoy a cigarette. I never suffered that delusion. I smoked because I thought it helped me to concentrate and because it helped my nerves. Now I am a non-smoker, the most difficult part is trying to believe that those days actually happened. It's like awakening from a nightmare, and that is about the size of it. Nicotine is a drug, and your senses are drugged – your taste buds, your sense of smell. The worst aspect of smoking isn't the injury to your health or pocket; it is the warping of the mind. You search for any plausible excuse to go on smoking.

I remember at one stage switching to a pipe, after a failed attempt to kick cigarettes, in the belief that it was less harmful and would cut down my intake.

Some of those pipe tobaccos are absolutely foul. The aroma can be pleasant but, to start with, they are awful to smoke. I can remember that for about three months the tip of my tongue was as sore as a boil. A liquid brown goo collects in the bottom of the bowl of the pipe. Occasionally you unwittingly bring the bowl above the horizontal and before you realize it you have swallowed a mouthful of the filthy stuff. The result is usually to throw up immediately, no matter what company you are in.

It took me three months to learn to cope with the pipe, but what I cannot understand is why I didn't sit down sometime during that three months and ask myself why I was submitting myself to the torture.

Of course, once they learn to cope with the pipe, no one appears more contented than pipe smokers. Most of them are convinced that they smoke because they enjoy the pipe. But why did they have to work so hard to learn to like it when they were perfectly happy without it?

The answer is that once you have become addicted to nicotine, the brainwashing is increased. Your subconscious mind knows that the little monster has to be fed, and you block everything else from your mind. As I have already stated, it is fear that keeps people smoking, the fear of that empty, insecure feeling that you get when you stop supplying the nicotine. Because you are not aware of it doesn't mean it isn't there. You don't have to understand it any more than a cat needs to understand where the underfloor hot-water pipes are; it just knows that if it sits in a certain place it gets the feeling of warmth.

It is the brainwashing that is the main difficulty in giving up smoking. The brainwashing of our upbringing in society reinforced with the brainwashing from our own addiction and, most powerful of all, the brainwashing of our friends, relatives and colleagues.

The only thing that persuades us to smoke in the first place is all the other people doing it. We feel we are missing out. We work so hard to become hooked, yet nobody ever finds out what they have been missing. But every time we see another smoker he reassures us that there must be something in it, otherwise he wouldn't be doing it. Even when he has kicked the habit, the ex-smoker feels he is being deprived when a smoker lights up at a party or other social function. He feels safe. He can have just one. And, before he knows it, he is hooked again.

This brainwashing is very powerful and you need to be aware of its effects. Many older smokers will remember the Paul Temple detective series that was a very popular radio programme after the war. One of the series was dealing with addiction to marijuana, commonly known as 'pot' or 'grass'. Unbeknown to the smoker, wicked men were selling cigarettes that contained 'pot'. There were no harmful effects. People merely became addicted and had to go on buying the cigarettes. (During my consultations literally hundreds of smokers have admitted to trying 'pot'. None of them said they became hooked on it.) I was about seven years old when I listened to the programme. It was my first knowledge of drug addiction. The concept of addiction, being compelled to go on taking the drug, filled me with horror, and even to this day, in spite of the fact that I am fairly convinced that 'pot' is not addictive, I would not dare take one puff of marijuana. How ironic that I should have ended up a junky on the world's No. 1 addictive drug. If only Paul Temple had warned me about the cigarette itself. How ironic too that over forty years later mankind spends thousands of dollars on cancer research, yet millions are spent persuading healthy teenagers to become hooked on the filthy weed, our own government having the largest vested interest.

We are about to remove the brainwashing. It is not the non-smoker who is being deprived but the poor smoker who is forfeiting a lifetime of:

HEALTH
ENERGY
WEALTH
PEACE OF MIND
CONFIDENCE
COURAGE
SELF-RESPECT
HAPPINESS.

And what does he gain from these considerable sacrifices?

ABSOLUTELY NOTHING – except the illusion of trying to get back to the state of peace, tranquillity and confidence that the non-smoker enjoys all the time.

8

Relieving Withdrawal Pangs

As I explained earlier, smokers think they smoke for enjoyment, relaxation or some sort of boost. In fact, this an illusion. The actual reason is the relief of withdrawal pangs.

In the early days we use the cigarette as a social prop. We can take it or leave it. However, the subtle chain has started. Our subconscious mind begins to learn that a cigarette taken at certain times tends to be pleasurable.

The more we become hooked on the drug, the greater the need to relieve the withdrawal pangs and the further the cigarette drags you down and the more you are fooled into believing it is doing the opposite. It all happens so slowly, so gradually, you are not even aware of it. Each day you feel no different from the day before. Most smokers don't even realize they are hooked until they actually try to stop, and even then many won't admit to it. A few stalwarts just keep their heads in the sand all their lives, trying to convince themselves and other people that they enjoy it.

I have had the following conversation with hundreds of teenagers.

ME: You realize that nicotine is a drug and that the only reason why you are smoking is that you cannot stop.

T: Nonsense! I enjoy it. If I didn't, I would stop.

ME: Just stop for a week to prove to me you can if you want to.

T: No need. I enjoy it. If I wanted to stop, I would.

ME: Just stop for a week to prove to yourself you are not hooked.

T: What's the point? I enjoy it.

As already stated, smokers tend to relieve their withdrawal pangs at times of stress, boredom, concentration, relaxation or a combination of these. This point is explained in greater detail in the next few chapters.

9

The Stress Situation

I am referring not only to the great tragedies of life but also to the minor stresses, the socializing, the telephone call, the anxieties of the housewife with noisy young children and so on.

Let us use the telephone conversation as an example. For most people the telephone is slightly stressful, particularly for the business man. Most calls aren't from satisfied customers or your boss congratulating you. There's usually some sort of aggro – something going wrong or somebody making demands. At that time the smoker, if he isn't already doing so, will light up a cigarette. He doesn't know why he does this, but he does know that for some reason it appears to help.

What has actually happened is this. Without being conscious of it, he has already been suffering aggravation (i.e. the withdrawal pangs). By partially relieving that aggravation at the same time as normal stress, the total stress is reduced and the smoker gets a boost. At this point the boost is not, in fact, an illusion. The smoker will feel better than before he lit the cigarette. However, even when smoking that cigarette the smoker is more tense than if he were a non-smoker because the more you go into the drug, the more it knocks you down and the less it restores you when you smoke.

I promised no shock treatment. In the example I am about to give, I am not trying to shock you, I am merely emphasizing that cigarettes destroy your nerves rather than relax them.

Try to imagine getting to the stage where a doctor tells you that unless you stop smoking he is going to have to remove your legs. Just for a moment pause and try to visualize life without your legs. Try to imagine the frame of mind of a man who, issued with that warning, actually continues smoking and then has his legs removed.

I used to hear stories like that and dismissed them as cranky. In fact, I used to wish a doctor would tell me that; then I would have stopped. Yet I was already fully expecting any day to have a brain haemorrhage, and lose not only my legs but my life. I didn't think of myself as a crank, just a heavy smoker.

Such stories are not cranky. That is what this awful drug does to you. As you go through life it systematically takes away your nerve and courage. The more it takes your courage away, the more you are deluded into believing the cigarette is doing the opposite. We have all heard of the panic that overtakes smokers when they are out late at night and in fear of running out of cigarettes. Non-smokers do not suffer from it. The cigarette causes that feeling. At the same time, as you go through life the cigarette not only destroys your nerves but is a powerful poison, progressively destroying your physical health. By the time the smoker reaches the stage at which it is killing him, he believes the cigarette is his courage and cannot face life without it.

Get it clear in your head that the cigarette is not relieving your nerves; it is slowly but steadily destroying them. One of the great gains of breaking the habit is the return of your confidence and self-assurance.

10

The Boring Situation

If you are already smoking at this moment, you will probably have already forgotten about it until I reminded you.

Another fallacy about smoking is that cigarettes relieve boredom. Boredom is a frame of mind. When you smoke a cigarette your mind isn't saying, 'I'm smoking a cigarette. I'm smoking a cigarette.' The only time that happens is when you have been deprived for a long time or are trying to cut down, or during those first few cigarettes after a failed attempt to stop.

The true situation is this: when you are addicted to nicotine and are not smoking, there is something missing. If you have something to occupy your mind that isn't stressful, you can go for long periods without being bothered by the absence of the drug. However, when you are bored there's nothing to take your mind off it, so you feed the monster. When you are indulging yourself (i.e. not trying to stop or cut down), even lighting up becomes subconscious. Even pipe smokers and roll-your-own smokers can perform this ritual automatically. If any smoker tries to remember the cigarettes he has smoked during the day, he can only remember a small proportion of them – e.g. the first of the day or the one after a meal.

The truth is that cigarettes tend to increase boredom indirectly because they make you feel lethargic, and instead of undertaking some energetic activity smokers tend to lounge around, bored, relieving their withdrawal pangs.

11

The Concentration
Situation

Cigarettes do not help concentration. That is just an illusion.

When you are trying to concentrate, you automatically try to avoid distractions like feeling cold or hot. The smoker is already suffering: that little monster wants his fix. So when he wants to concentrate he doesn't even have to think about it. He automtically lights up, partially ending the craving, gets on with the matter in hand and has already forgotten that he is smoking.

Cigarettes do not help concentration. They help to ruin it because after a while, even while smoking a cigarette, the smoker's withdrawal pangs cease to be completely relieved. The smoker then increases his intake, and the problem then increases.

Concentration is also affected adversely for another reason. The progressive blocking up of the arteries and veins with poisons starves the brain of oxygen. In fact, your concentration and inspiration will be greatly improved as this process is reversed.

It was the concentration aspect that prevented me from succeeding when using the willpower method. I could put up with the irritability and bad temper, but when I really needed to concentrate on something difficult, I had to have that cigarette. I can well remember the panic I felt when I discovered that I was not allowed to smoke during my accountancy exams. I was already a chain-smoker and convinced that I would not be able to concentrate for three hours without a cigarette. But I passed the exams, and I can't even remember thinking about smoking at the time, so, when it came to the crunch, it obviously didn't bother me.

The loss of concentration that smokers suffer when they try to stop smoking is not, in fact, due to the physical withdrawal from nicotine. When you are a smoker, you have mental blocks. When you have one, what do you do? If you are not already smoking one, you light a cigarette. That doesn't cure the mental block, so then what do you do? You do what you have to do: you get on with it, just as non-smokers do. When you are a smoker nothing gets blamed on the cigarette. Smokers never have smoking coughs; they just have permanent colds. The moment you stop smoking everything that goes wrong in your life is blamed on the fact that you've stopped smoking. Now when you have a mental block, instead of just getting on with it you start to say, 'If only I could light up now, it would solve my problem.' You then start to question your decision to quit smoking.

If you believe that smoking is a genuine aid to concentration, then worrying about it will guarantee that you won't be able to concentrate. It's the doubting, not the physical withdrawal pangs, that causes the problem. Always remember: it is smokers who suffer withdrawal pangs and not non-smokers.

When I extinguished my last cigarette I went overnight from a hundred a day to zero without any apparent loss of concentration.

12

The Relaxing Situation

Most smokers think that a cigarette helps to relax them. The truth is that nicotine is a chemical stimulant. If you take your pulse and then smoke two consecutive cigarettes, there will be a marked increase in your pulse rate.

One of the favourite cigarettes for most smokers is the one after a meal. A meal is a time of day when we stop working; we sit down and relax, relieve our hunger and thirst and are then completely satisfied. However, the poor smoker cannot relax, as he has another hunger to satisfy. He thinks of the cigarette as the icing on the cake, but it is the little monster that needs feeding.

The truth is that the nicotine addict can never be completely relaxed, and as you go through life the worse it gets.

The most unrelaxed people on this planet aren't non-smokers but fifty-year-old business executives who chain-smoke, are permanently coughing and spluttering, have high blood pressure and are constantly irritable. At this point cigarettes cease to relieve even partially the symptoms that they have created.

I can remember when I was a young accountant, bringing up a family. One of my children would do something wrong and I would lose my temper to an extent that was out of all proportion to what he had done. I really believed that I had an evil demon in my make-up. I now know that it was the cigarettes that were creating the problem. During those times I thought I had all the problems in the world, but when I look back on my life I wonder where all the great stress was. In everything else in my life I was in control. The one thing that controlled me was the smoking. The sad thing is that even today I can't convince my children that it was the smoking that caused me to be so irritable. Every time they hear a smoker trying to justify his addiction, the message is 'Oh, they calm me. They help me to relax.'

A couple of years ago, the adoption authorities threatened to prevent smokers from adopting children. A man rang up, irate. He said, 'You are completely wrong. I can remember when I was a child, if I had a contentious matter to raise with my mother, I would wait until she lit a cigarette because she was more relaxed then.' Why couldn't he talk to his mother when she wasn't smoking a cigarette? Why are smokers so unrelaxed when they are not smoking, even after a meal at a restaurant? Why are non-smokers completely relaxed then? Why are smokers not able to relax without a cigarette? The next time you are in a supermarket and you see a young housewife screaming at a child, just watch her leave. The first thing she will do is to light a cigarette. Remember seeing, say, Steve Davis and Hurricane Higgins on television? Notice the difference? Which of the two was more relaxed? Start watching smokers, particularly when they are not allowed to smoke. You'll find that they have their hands near their mouths, or they are twiddling their hands, or tapping their feet, or fiddling with their hair, or clenching their jaw. Smokers aren't relaxed. They've forgotten what it feels like to be completely relaxed. That's one of the many joys they have to come.

The whole business of smoking can be likened to a fly being caught in a pitcher plant. To begin with, the fly is eating the nectar. At some imperceptible stage the plant begins to eat the fly.

Isn't it time you climbed out of that plant?

13

Combination Cigarettes

No, a combination cigarette is not when you are smoking two or more at the same time. It is when that happens to you that you begin to wonder why you were smoking the first one. I once burnt the back of my hand trying to put a cigarette in my mouth when there was already one there. Actually, it is not quite as stupid as you think. As I have already said, eventually the cigarette ceases to relieve the withdrawal pangs, and even when you are smoking the cigarette there is still something missing. This is the terrible frustration of the chain smoker. Whenever you need the boost, you are already smoking, and this is why heavy smokers turn to drink or other drugs. But I digress.

A combination cigarette is one occasioned by two or more of our usual reasons for smoking, e.g. social functions, parties, weddings, meals in restaurants. These are examples of occasions that are both stressful and relaxing. This might at first appear to be a contradiction, but it isn't. Any form of socializing can be stressful, even with friends, and at the same time you want to be enjoying yourself and be completely relaxed.

There are situations where all four reasons are present at one and the same time. Driving can be one of these. If you are leaving a tense situation, like a visit to the dentist or the doctor, you can now relax. At the same time driving always involves an element of stress. Your life is at stake. You are also having to concentrate. You may not be aware of the last two factors, but the fact that they are subconscious doesn't mean they aren't there. And if you are stuck in a traffic jam, or have a long motorway drive, you may also be bored.

Another classic example is a game of cards. If it's a game like bridge or poker, you have to concentrate. If you are losing more than you can afford, it is stressful. If you have long periods of not getting a decent hand, it can be boring. And, while all this is going on, you are at leisure; you are supposed to be relaxing. During a game of cards, no matter how slight the withdrawal pangs are, all smokers will be chain-smoking, even otherwise casual smokers. The ashtrays will fill and overflow in no time. There'll be a constant fall-out cloud above head height. If you were to tap any of the smokers on the shoulder and ask him if he was enjoying it, the answer would be 'You have got to be joking.' It is often after nights like these, when we wake up with a throat like a cess pit, that we decide to stop smoking.

These combination cigarettes are often special ones, the ones that we think we'll miss most when we are contemplating giving up smoking. We think that life will never be quite as enjoyable again. In fact, it is the same principle at work: these cigarettes simply provide relief from withdrawal pangs, and at certain times we have greater need to relieve them than at others.

Let us make it quite clear. It is not the cigarette that is special; it is the occasion. Once we have removed the need for the cigarette, such occasions will become more enjoyable and the stress situation less stressful. This will be explained in great detail in the next chapter.

14

What am I Giving Up?

ABSOLUTELY NOTHING! The thing that makes it difficult for us to give up is fear. The fear that we are being deprived of our pleasure or prop. The fear that certain pleasant situations will never be quite the same again. The fear of being unable to cope with stressful situations.

In other words, the effect of brainwashing is to delude us into believing that there is a weakness in us, or something inherent in the cigarette that we need, and that when we stop smoking there will be a void.

Get it clear in your mind: CIGARETTES DO NOT FILL A VOID. THEY CREATE IT!

These bodies of ours are the most sophisticated objects on this planet. Whether you believe in a creator, a process of natural selection or a combination of both, whatever being or system devised these bodies of ours, it is a thousand times more effective than man! Man cannot create the smallest living cell, let alone the miracle of eyesight, reproduction, our circulatory system or our brains. If the creator or process had intended us to smoke, we would have been provided with some filter device to keep the poisons out of our bodies and some sort of chimney.

Our bodies are, in fact, provided with failsafe warning devices in the form of the cough, dizziness, sickness, etc., and we ignore these at our peril.

The beautiful truth is – there is nothing to give up. Once you purge that little monster from your body and the brainwashing from your mind, you will neither want cigarettes nor need them.

Cigarettes do not improve meals. They ruin them. They destroy your sense of taste and smell. Observe smokers in a restaurant, smoking between courses. It is not the meal that they are enjoying; they cannot wait for the meal to be over, as it is interfering with the cigarettes. Many of them do it in spite of the fact that they know it causes offence to non-smokers. It is not that smokers are generally inconsiderate people; it is just that they are miserable without the cigarette. They are between the devil and the deep blue sea. They either have to abstain and be miserable because they cannot smoke, or smoke and be miserable because they are offending other people, feel guilty and despise themselves for it.

Watch smokers at an official function where they have to wait for the loyal toast. Many of them develop weak bladders and have to sneak off for the crafty puff. That is when you see smoking for the true addiction that it is. Smokers do not smoke because they enjoy it. They do it because they are miserable without it.

Because many of us start smoking on social occasions when we are young and shy, we acquire the belief that we cannot enjoy social occasions without a cigarette. This is nonsense. Tobacco takes away your confidence. The greatest evidence of the fear that cigarettes instil in smokers is their effect on women. Practically all women are fastidious about their personal appearance. They wouldn't dream of appearing at a social function not immaculately turned out and smelling beautifully. Yet knowing that their breath smells like a stale ashtray does not seem to deter them in the least. I know that it *bothers* them greatly – many hate the smell of their own hair and clothes – yet it doesn't *deter* them. Such is the fear that this awful drug instils in the smoker.

Cigarettes do not help social occasions; they destroy them. Having to hold a drink in one hand and a cigarette in the other, trying to dispose of the ash and the continual chain of dogends, trying not to breathe smoke and fumes into the face of the person you are conversing with, wondering whether they can smell your breath or see the stains on your teeth.

Not only is there nothing to give up, but there are marvellous positive gains. When smokers contemplate giving up smoking they tend to concentrate on health, money and social stigma. These are obviously valid and important issues, but I personally believe the greatest gains from giving up are psychological, and for varying reasons they include:

1 The return of your confidence and courage.
2 Freedom from the slavery.
3 Not to have to go through life suffering the awful black shadows at the back of your mind, knowing you are being despised by half of the population and, worst of all, despising yourself.

Not only is life better as a non-smoker but it is infinitely more enjoyable. I do not only mean you will be healthier and wealthier. I mean you will be happier and enjoy life far more.

The marvellous gains from being a non-smoker are discussed in the next few chapters.

Some smokers find it difficult to appreciate this 'void' concept, and the following analogy may assist you.

Imagine having a cold sore on your face. I've got this marvellous ointment. I say to you, 'Try this stuff.' You rub the ointment on, and the sore disappears immediately. A week later it reappears. You ask, 'Do you have any more of that ointment?' I say, 'Keep the tube. You might need it again.' You apply the ointment. Hey presto, the sore disappears again. Every time the sore returns, it gets larger and more painful and the interval gets shorter and shorter. Eventually the sore covers your whole face and is excruciatingly painful. It is now returning every half hour. You know that the ointment will remove it temporarily, but you are very worried. Will the sore eventually spread over your whole body? Will the interval disappear completely? You go to your doctor. He can't cure it. You try other things, but nothing helps except this marvellous ointment.

By now you are completely dependent on the ointment. You never go out without ensuring that you have a tube of the ointment with you. If you go abroad, you make sure that you take several tubes with you. Now, in addition to your worries about your health, I'm charging you $200 per tube. You have no choice but to pay.

You then read in the medical column of your newspaper that this isn't happening just to you; many other people have been suffering from the same problem. In fact, pharmacists have discovered that the ointment doesn't actually cure the sore. All that it does is to take the sore beneath the surface of the skin. It is the ointment that has caused the sore to grow. All you have to do to get rid of the sore is to stop using the ointment. The sore will eventually disappear in due course.

Would you continue to use the ointment?

Would it take will power not to use the ointment? If you didn't believe the article, there might be a few days of apprehension, but once you realized that the sore was beginning to get better, the need or desire to use the ointment would go.

Would you be miserable? Of course you wouldn't. You had an awful problem, which you thought was insoluble. Now you've

43

found the solution. Even if it took a year for that sore to disappear completely, each day, as it improved, you'd think, 'Isn't it marvellous? I'm not going to die.'

This was the magic that happened to me when I extinguished that final cigarette. Let me make one point quite clear in the analogy of the sore and the ointment. The sore isn't lung cancer, or arterial sclerosis, or emphysema, or angina, or chronic asthma, or bronchitis, or coronary heart disease. They are all in addition to the sore. It isn't the thousands of pounds that we burn, or the lifetime of bad breath and stained teeth, the lethargy, the wheezing and coughing, the years we spend choking ourselves and wishing we didn't, the times when we are being punished because we are not allowed to smoke. It isn't the lifetime of being despised by other people, or, worst of all, despising yourself. These are all in addition to the sore. The sore is what makes us close our minds to all these things. It's that panic feeling of 'I want a cigarette.' Non-smokers don't suffer from that feeling. The worst thing we ever suffer from is fear, and the greatest gain you will receive is to be rid of that fear.

It was as if a great mist had suddenly lifted from my mind. I could see so clearly that that panic feeling of wanting a cigarette wasn't some sort of weakness in me, or some magic quality in the cigarette. It was caused by the first cigarette; and each subsequent one, far from relieving the feeling, was causing it. At the same time I could see that all these other happy smokers were going through the same nightmare that I was. Not as bad as mine, but all putting up phoney arguments to try to justify their stupidity.

IT'S SO NICE TO BE FREE!

15

Self-imposed Slavery

Usually when smokers try to stop the main reasons are health, money, and social stigma. Part of the brainwashing of this awful drug is the sheer slavery.

Man fought hard in the last century to abolish slavery, and yet the smoker spends his life suffering self-imposed slavery. He seems to be oblivious to the fact that, when he is allowed to smoke, he wishes that he were a non-smoker. With most of the cigarettes we smoke in our lives, not only do we not enjoy them but we aren't even aware that we are smoking them. It is only after a period of abstinence that we actually suffer the delusion of enjoying a cigarette (e.g. the first in the morning, the one after a meal, etc.).

The only time that the cigarette becomes precious is when we are trying to cut down or abstain, or when society tries to force us to (e.g. when attending churches, hospitals, supermarkets, theatres and so on).

The confirmed smoker should bear in mind that this trend will get worse and worse. Today it is trains. Tomorrow it will be all public places.

Gone are the days when the smoker could enter a friend's or stranger's house and say, 'Do you mind if I smoke?' Nowadays the poor smoker, on entering a strange house, will search desperately for an ashtray and hope to find dogends in it. If there is no ashtray, he will generally try to last out, and if he cannot, he will ask for permission to smoke and is likely to be told: 'Smoke if you have to,' or 'Well, we would rather you didn't. The smell seems to linger so.'

The poor smoker, who was already feeling wretched, wants the ground to open up and swallow him.

I remember during my smoking days, every time I went to church, it was an ordeal. Even during my own daughter's wedding, when I should have been standing there a proud father, what was I doing? I was thinking, 'Let's get on with it, so that we can get outside and have a drag.'

It will help you to observe smokers on these occasions. They huddle together. There is never just one packet. There are twenty packets being thrust about, and the conversation is always the same.

'Do you smoke?'

'Yes, but have one of mine.'

'I will have one of yours later.'

They light up and take a deep drag, thinking, 'Aren't we lucky? We have got our little reward. The poor non-smoker hasn't got a reward.'

The poor non-smoker doesn't need a reward. We were not designed to go through life systematically poisoning our own bodies. The pathetic thing is that even when smoking a cigarette, the smoker doesn't achieve the feeling of peace, confidence and tranquillity that the non-smoker has experienced for the whole of his non-smoking life. The non-smoker isn't sitting in the church feeling agitated and wishing his life away. He can enjoy the whole of his life.

I can also remember playing indoor bowls in the winter and pretending to have a weak bladder in order to nip off for a puff. No, this wasn't a fourteen-year-old schoolboy but a forty-year-old chartered accountant. How pathetic. And even when I was back playing the game I wasn't enjoying it. I was looking forward to the finish so that I could smoke again, yet this was supposed to be my way of relaxing and enjoying my favourite hobby.

To me one of the tremendous joys of being a non-smoker is to be freed from that slavery, to be able to enjoy the whole of my life and not spend half of it craving for a cigarette and then, when I light up, wishing I didn't have to do it.

Smokers should bear in mind that when they are in the houses of non-smokers or even in the company of non-smokers, it is not the self-righteous non-smoker who is depriving them but the 'little monster'.

16

I'll Save $40.00 per Week

I cannot repeat too often that it is brainwashing that makes it difficult to stop smoking, and the more brainwashing we can dispel before we start, the easier you will find it to achieve your goal.

Occasionally I get into arguments with people whom I call confirmed smokers. By my definition a confirmed smoker is somebody who can afford it, doesn't believe it injures his health and isn't worried about the social stigma. (There are not many about nowadays.)

If he is a young man, I say to him, 'I cannot believe you are not worried about the money you are spending.'

Usually his eyes light up. If I had attacked him on health grounds or on the social stigma, he would feel at a disadvantage, but on money – 'Oh, I can afford it. It is only $40.00 per week and I think it is worth it. It is my only vice or pleasure,' etc.

If he is a twenty-per-day smoker I say to him, 'I still cannot believe you are not worried about the money. You are going to spend about $60,000 in your lifetime. What are you doing with that money? You are not even setting light to it or throwing it away. You are actually using that money to ruin your physical health, to destroy your nerves and confidence, to suffer a lifetime of slavery, a lifetime of bad breath and stained teeth. Surely that must worry you?'

It is apparent at this point, particularly with young smokers, that they have never considered it a lifetime expense. For most smokers the price of a packet is bad enough. Occasionally we work out what we spend in a week, and that is alarming. Very occasionally (and only when we think about stopping) we estimate what we spend in a year and that is frightening, but over a lifetime – it is unthinkable.

However, because it is an argument the confirmed smoker will say, 'I can afford it. It is only so much a week.' He does an 'encyclopedia salesman' on himself.

I then say, 'I will make you an offer you cannot refuse. You pay me $2,000 now, and I will provide you with free cigarettes for the rest of your life.'

If I were offering to take over a $60,000 mortgage for $2,000, the smoker would have my signature on a piece of paper before I could move, and yet not one confirmed smoker (and please bear in mind I am not now talking to someone like yourself who plans to stop, I am talking to someone who has no intention of stopping), has ever taken me up on that offer. Why not?

Often at this point in my consultation, a smoker will say, 'Look, I am not really worried about the money aspect.' If you are thinking along these lines, ask yourself why you are not worried. Why in other aspects of life you will go to a great deal of trouble to save a few dollars here and there and yet spend thousands of dollars poisoning yourself and hang the expense?

The answer to these questions is this. Every other decision that you make in your life will be the result of an analytical process of weighing up the pros and cons and arriving at a rational answer. It may be the wrong answer, but at least it will be the result of rational deduction. Whenever any smoker weighs up the pros and cons of smoking, the answer is a dozen times over: 'STOP SMOKING! YOU ARE A MUG!' Therefore all smokers are smoking not because they want to or because they decided to but because they think they cannot stop. They have to brainwash themselves. They have to keep their heads in the sand.

The strange thing is smokers will arrange pacts among themselves, such as 'First one to give in pays the other $100', yet the thousands of dollars that they would save by stopping don't seem to affect them. This is because they are still thinking with the brainwashed mind of the smoker.

Just take the sand out of your eyes for a moment. Smoking is a chain reaction and a chain for life. If you do not break that chain, you will remain a smoker for the rest of your life. Now estimate how much you think you will spend on smoking the rest of your life. The amount will obviously vary with each individual, but for the purpose of this exercise let us assume it is $20,000.

You will shortly be making the decision to smoke your final cigarette (not yet, please – remember the initial instructions). All you have to do to remain a non-smoker is not to fall for the trap again. That is, do not smoke that first cigarette. If you do, that one cigarette will cost you $20,000.

If you think this is a trick way of looking at it, you are still kidding yourself. Just work out now much money you would have saved if you hadn't smoked your first cigarette.

If you see the argument as factual, ask yourself how you would feel if there were a cheque from a lottery for $20,000 on your carpet tomorrow. You'd be dancing with delight! So start dancing! You are about to start receiving that bonus, and that's just one of the several marvellous gains you are about to receive.

During the withdrawal period you may be tempted to have just one final cigarette. It will help you to resist the temptation if you remind yourself it will cost you $20,000 (or whatever your estimate is)!

I've been making that offer on television and radio programmes for years. I still find it incredible that not one confirmed smoker has ever taken my offer up. There are members of my golf club whom I taunt every time I hear them complain about an increase in tobacco prices. In fact, I'm frightened that if I goad them too much, one of them will take me up on it. I'd lose a fortune if he did.

If you are in the company of happy, cheerful smokers who tell you how much they enjoy it, just tell them that you know an idiot who, if you pay him a year's smoking money in advance, will provide you with free cigarettes for the rest of your life. Perhaps you can find me someone who will take up the offer?

17

Health

This is the area where the brainwashing is the greatest. Smokers think they are aware of the health risks. They are not.

Even in my case, when I was expecting my head to explode any moment and honestly believed I was prepared to accept the consequences, I was still kidding myself.

If in those days I had taken a cigarette out of the packet and a red bleeper started to sound, followed by a warning voice saying, 'OK, Allen, this is the one! Fortunately you do get a warning, and this is it. Up to now you have got away with it, but if you smoke another cigarette your head will explode,' do you think I would have lit that cigarette?

If you are in doubt about the answer, just try walking up to a main road with busy traffic, stand on the kerb with your eyes closed and try to imagine you have the choice of either stopping smoking or walking blindfolded across the road before taking your next cigarette.

There is no doubt what your choice would be. I had been doing what every smoker does all his smoking life: closing my mind and keeping my head in the sand, hoping that I would wake up one morning and just not want to smoke any more. Smokers cannot allow themselves to think of the health risks. If they do, even the illusion of enjoying the habit goes.

This explains why the shock treatment used by the media on National No-Smoking Days is so ineffective. It is only non-smokers who can bring themselves to watch. It also explains why smokers, recalling Uncle Fred who smoked forty a day and lived until he was eighty, will ignore the thousands of people who are brought down in their prime because of this poisonous weed.

About six times a week I have the following conversation with smokers (usually the younger ones):

ME: Why do you want to stop?
SMOKER: I can't afford it.
ME: Aren't you worried about the health risks?
SMOKER: No. I could step under a bus tomorrow.
ME: Would you deliberately step under a bus?
SMOKER: Of course not.
ME: Do you not bother to look left and right when you cross the road?
SMOKER: Of course I do.

Exactly. The smoker goes to a lot of trouble not to step under a bus, and the odds are hundreds of thousands to one against it happening. Yet the smoker risks the near certainty of being crippled by the weed and appears to be completely oblivious to the risks. Such is the power of the brainwashing.

I remember one famous British golfer who wouldn't go on the American circuit because he was afraid of flying. Yet he would chain-smoke round the golf course. Isn't it strange that, if we felt there was the slightest fault in an aeroplane, we wouldn't go up in it, even though the risks are hundreds of thousands to one against death, yet we take a one-in-four certainty with the cigarette and are apparently oblivious to it. And what does the smoker get out of it?

ABSOLUTELY NOTHING!

Another common myth about smoking is the smoker's cough. Many of the younger people who come to see me are not worried about their health because they do not cough. The true facts are just the reverse. A cough is one of nature's fail-safe methods of dispelling foreign matter from the lungs. The cough itself is not a disease; it is just a symptom. When smokers cough it is because their lungs are trying to dispel cancer-triggering tars and poisons. When they do not cough those tars and poisons remain in their lungs, and that is when they cause cancer.

Just think of it this way. If you had a nice car and allowed it to rust without doing anything about it, that would be pretty stupid, as it would soon be a heap of rust and would not carry you about. However, that would not be the end of the world; it is only a question of money and you could always buy a new one. Your body is the vehicle that carries you through life. We all say that our health is our most valued asset. How true that is, as sick millionaires will tell you. Most of us can look back at some illness or

51

accident in our lives when we prayed to get better. (HOW SOON WE FORGET.) By being a smoker you are not only letting rust get in and doing nothing about it; you are systematically destroying the vehicle you need to go through life, and you only get one.

Wise up. You don't have to do it, and remember: it is doing ABSOLUTELY NOTHING FOR YOU.

Just for a moment take your head out of the sand and ask yourself, if you knew for certain that the next cigarette would be the one to trigger off cancer in your body, whether you would actually smoke it. Forget the disease (it is difficult to imagine it), but imagine you have to go to the Royal Marsden to suffer those awful tests – radium treatment, etc. Now you are not planning the rest of your life. You are planning your death. What is going to happen to your family and loved ones, your plans and dreams?

I often see the people that it happens to. They didn't think it would happen to them either, and the worst thing about it isn't the disease itself but the knowledge they have brought it on themselves. All our lives as smokers we are saying, 'I'll stop tomorrow.' Try to imagine how those people feel who 'hit the button'. For them the brainwashing is ended. They then see the habit as it really is and spend the remainder of their lives thinking, 'Why did I kid myself I needed to smoke? If I only had the chance to go back!'

Stop kidding yourself. You have the chance. It's a chain reaction. If you smoke the next cigarette, it will lead to the next one and the next. It's already happening to you.

At the beginning of the book I promised you no shock treatment. If you have already decided you are going to stop smoking, this isn't shock treatment for you. If you are still in doubt, skip the remainder of this chapter and come back to it when you have read the rest of the book.

Volumes of statistics have already been written about the damage that cigarettes can cause to the smoker's health. The trouble is that until the smoker decides to stop he doesn't want to know. Even that government health warning is a waste of time because the smoker puts blinkers on, and if he inadvertently reads it, the first thing he does is light up a cigarette.

Smokers tend to think of the health hazard as a hit-and-miss affair, like stepping on a mine. Get it into your head: it is already happening. Every time you puff on a cigarette you are breathing cancer-triggering tars into your lungs, and cancer is by no means the worst of the killer diseases that cigarettes cause or contribute to. They are also a powerful contributory cause of heart disease, arteriosclerosis, emphysema, angina, thrombosis, chronic bronchitis and asthma.

Smokers also suffer the illusion that the ill-effects of smoking are overstated. The reverse is the case. There is no doubt that cigarettes are the No. 1 cause of death in Western society. The trouble is that in many cases where cigarettes cause the death or are a contributory factor, it is not blamed on cigarettes in the statistics.

It has been estimated that 44 per cent of household fires are caused by cigarettes, and I wonder how many road accidents have been caused by cigarettes during that split second when you take your eye off the road to light up.

I am normally a careful driver, but the nearest I came to death (except from smoking itself) was when trying to roll a cigarette while driving, and I hate to think of the number of times I coughed a cigarette out of my mouth while driving – it always seemed to end up between the seats. I am sure many other smoking drivers have had the experience of trying to locate the burning cigarette with one hand while trying to drive with the other.

The effect of the brainwashing is that we tend to think like the man who, having fallen off a 100-storey building, is heard to say, as he passes the fiftieth floor, 'So far, so good!' We think that as we have got away with it so far, one more cigarette won't make the difference.

Trying to see it another way, the 'habit' is a continuous chain for life, each cigarette creating the need for the next. When you start the habit you light a fuse. The trouble is, YOU DON'T KNOW HOW LONG THE FUSE IS. Every time that you light a cigarette you are one step near to the bomb exploding. HOW WILL YOU KNOW IF IT'S THE NEXT ONE?

18

Energy

Most smokers are aware of congesting their lungs, but many are not aware of the general lethargy that smoking causes.

In addition to congesting the lungs, the smoker is progressively gunging up his arteries and veins with poisons such as nicotine, carbon monoxide and others.

Our lungs and bloodstream are intended to carry oxygen and other nutrients to the various organs and muscles of our body. The smoker is increasingly starving every muscle and organ of his body of oxygen, so that they are daily functioning less efficiently, and he is not only becoming more and more lethargic each day but also has less resistance to other diseases.

Because it all happens so slowly and gradually, the smoker is unaware that it is happening. Each day he feels no different from the previous day; because he doesn't feel ill, he tends to regard the permanent state of lethargy as getting old.

From being a very fit teenager I was permanently tired for thirty-odd years. I thought it was only children and teenagers who had energy. One of the marvellous bonuses for me, shortly after stopping, was suddenly to have energy again, to actually want to exercise.

This abusing of the body and the lack of energy leads generally to other abuses. The smoker tends to avoid sporting activities and other pastimes and leans towards over-eating and drinking.

19

It Relaxes Me and Gives Me Confidence

This is the worst fallacy of all about smoking, and for me it ranks with the ending of the slavery, the greatest benefit of giving up smoking – not to have to go through life with the permanent feeling of insecurity that smokers suffer from.

Smokers find it very difficult to believe that the cigarette actually causes that insecure feeling you get when you are out late at night and running out of cigarettes. Non-smokers do not suffer from that feeling. It is the tobacco that causes it.

I only became aware of many of the advantages of giving up smoking months after I stopped, as a result of my consultations with other smokers.

For twenty-five years I refused to have a medical. If I wanted life assurance, I insisted on 'no medical' and paid higher premiums as a result. I hated visiting hospitals, doctors or dentists. I couldn't face the thought of getting old, pensions and so on.

None of these things did I relate to my smoking habit, but getting off it has been like awakening from a bad dream. Nowadays I look forward to each day. Of course, bad things happen in my life, and I am subject to the normal stresses and strains, but it is wonderful to have the confidence to cope with them, and extra health, energy and confidence make the good times more enjoyable too.

20

Those Sinister Black Shadows

Another of the great joys of giving up the weed is to be free of those sinister black shadows at the back of our minds.

All smokers know they are mugs and close their minds to the ill-effects of smoking. For most of our lives smoking is automatic, but the black shadows are always lurking in our subconscious minds, just beneath the surface.

Throughout our smoking lives there are moments when these black shadows are brought to the surface:

when we see that government health warning

a cancer scare

National No-Smoking Day

a coughing fit

a pain in the chest

the pained look of one of our children, friends or relatives

the awareness of our bad breath and stained teeth at the dentist
    or when kissing or conversing with a non-smoker

the loss of self-respect associated with being a smoker.

Even when we are not conscious of these things, those black shadows are always lurking just beneath the surface and the tug of war will get worse and worse the further you get into the 'habit'. It won't end until you decide to rid yourself of this awful addiction.

I cannot emphasize enough how marvellous it is to be free finally of those awful black shadows, to know that you do not have to smoke any more.

The last two chapters have dealt with the considerable advantages of being a non-smoker. I feel it necessary to give a balanced account, so the next chapter lists the advantages of being a smoker.

21

The Advantages of
Being a Smoker

22

The Willpower Method of Stopping

It is an accepted fact in our society that it is very difficult to give up smoking. Even books advising you how to do so usually start off by telling you how difficult it is. The truth is that it is ridiculously easy. Yes, I can understand your questioning that statement, but just consider it.

If your aim is to run a mile in under four minutes, that's difficult. You may have to sustain years of hard training, and even then you may be physically incapable of doing it. (Much of our achievement lies in the mind. Isn't it strange how difficult it was until Bannister actually did it but nowadays it is commonplace?)

However, in order to stop smoking all you have to do is not smoke any more. No one forces you to smoke (apart from yourself) and, unlike food or drink, you don't need it to survive. So if you want to stop doing it, why should it be difficult? In fact, it isn't. It is smokers who make it difficult by using the Willpower Method. I define the Willpower Method as any method that forces the smoker to feel he is making some sort of sacrifice. Let us just consider the Willpower Method.

We do not decide to become smokers. We merely experiment with the first few cigarettes and because they taste awful we are convinced that we can stop whenever we want to. In the main, we smoke those first few cigarettes only when we want to, and that is usually in the company of other smokers on social occasions.

Before we realize it, we are not only buying them regularly and smoking when we want to; we are smoking continuously.

It usually takes us a long time to realize that we are hooked because we suffer from the illusion that smokers smoke because they enjoy a cigarette, not because they have to have a cigarette. While we are not enjoying them (which we never do), we suffer from the illusion that we can stop whenever we want to.

Usually it is not until we actually try to stop that we realize a problem exists. The first attempts to stop are more often than not in the early days and are usually triggered off by shortage of money (boy meets girl and they are saving to set up home and do not want to waste money on cigarettes) or health (the teenager is still active in sport and finds he is short of breath). Whatever the reason, the smoker always waits for a stress situation, whether it be health or money. As soon as he stops, the little monster needs feeding. The smoker then wants a cigarette, and because he cannot have one this makes him more distressed. The thing he usually takes to relieve stress is now not available, so he suffers a triple blow. The probable result after a period of torture is the compromise 'I'll cut down' or 'I've picked the wrong time' or 'I'll wait until the stress has gone from my life.' However, once the stress has gone, he has no need to stop and doesn't decide to do so again until the next stressful time. Of course, the time is never right because life for most people doesn't become less stressful; it becomes more so. We leave the protection of our parents and enter the world of setting up home, taking on mortgages, having children, more responsible jobs, etc. Of course, the smoker's life can never become less stressful because it is the cigarette that actually causes stress. As the smoker's rate of nicotine intake rises, the more distressed he becomes and the greater the illusion of his dependency becomes.

In fact, it is an illusion that life becomes more stressful, and it's the smoking itself, or a similar crutch, that creates the illusion. This will be discussed in greater detail in chapter 28.

After the initial failures the smoker usually relies on the possibility that one day he will wake up and just not want to smoke any more. This hope is usually kindled by the stories that he has heard about other ex-smokers (e.g. 'I had a bout of 'flu and afterwards I didn't want to smoke any more').

Don't kid yourself. I have probed all of these rumours, and they are never quite as simple as they appear. Usually the smoker has already been preparing himself to stop and merely used the 'flu as a springboard. I spent thirty-odd years waiting to wake up one morning wanting never to smoke again. Whenever I had a bad chest I would look forward to its ending because it was interfering with my smoking.

More often in the case of people who stop 'just like that' they have suffered a shock. Perhaps a close relative has died from a cigarette-related disease or they have had a scare themselves. It is so much easier to say, 'I just decided to stop one day. That's the sort of chap I am.' Stop kidding yourself! It won't happen unless you make it happen.

Let's consider in greater detail why the Willpower Method is so difficult. For most of our lives we adopt the head-in-the-sand, 'I'll stop tomorrow' approach.

At odd times something will trigger off an attempt to stop. It may be concern about health, money, social stigma or we may have been going through a particularly heavy bout of choking and realize that we don't actually enjoy it.

Whatever the reason, we take our head out of the sand and start weighing up the pros and cons of smoking. We then find out what we have known all our lives: on a rational assessment the conclusion is, a dozen times over, STOP SMOKING.

If you were to sit down and give points out of ten to all the advantages of stopping and do a similar exercise with the advantages of smoking, the total point count for stopping would far outweigh the disadvantages.

However, although the smoker knows that he will be better off as a non-smoker, he does believe that he is making a sacrifice. Although it is an illusion, it is a *powerful* illusion. The smoker doesn't know why, but he believes that during the good times and the bad times of life the cigarette does appear to help.

Before he starts the attempt he has the brainwashing of our society, reinforced by the brainwashing of his own addiction. To these must be added the even more powerful brainwashing of 'how difficult it is to give up'.

He has heard stories of smokers who have stopped for many months and are still desperately craving a cigarette. There are all the disgruntled stoppers (people who stop and then spend the rest of their lives bemoaning the fact that they'd love a cigarette). He has heard of smokers who have stopped for many years, apparently leading happy lives, but have one cigarette and are suddenly hooked again. Probably he also knows several smokers in the advanced stages of the disease who are visibly destroying themselves and are clearly not enjoying cigarettes – yet they continue to smoke. Added to all this, he has probably already suffered one or more of these experiences himself.

So, instead of starting with the feeling 'Great! Have you heard the news? I haven't got to smoke any more,' he starts with a feeling of doom and gloom, as if he were trying to climb Everest, and he firmly believes that once the little monster has got his hooks into you, you are hooked for life. Many smokers even start

61

the attempt by apologizing to their friends and relatives: 'Look, I am trying to give up smoking. I will probably be irritable during the next few weeks. Try to bear with me.' Most attempts are doomed before they start.

Let's assume that the smoker survives a few days without a cigarette. The congestion is rapidly disappearing from his lungs. He hasn't bought cigarettes and consequently has more money in his pocket. So the reasons why he decided to stop in the first place are rapidly disappearing from his thoughts. It is like seeing a bad road accident when you are driving. It slows you down for a while, but the next time you are late for an appointment you have forgotten all about it and your foot stamps on the throttle.

On the other side of the tug of war, that little monster inside your stomach hasn't had his fix. There is no physical pain; if you had the same feeling because of a cold, you wouldn't stop working or get depressed. You would laugh it off. All the smoker knows is that he wants a cigarette. Quite why it is so important to him he doesn't know. The little monster in the stomach then starts off the big monster in the mind, and now the person who a few hours or days earlier was listing all the reasons to stop is desperately searching for any excuse to start again. Now he is saying things like:

1 Life is too short. The bomb could go off. I could step under a bus tomorrow. I have left it too late. They tell you everything gives you cancer these days.
2 I have picked the wrong time. I should have waited until after Christmas/after my holidays/after this stressful event in my life.
3 I cannot concentrate. I am getting irritable and bad tempered. I cannot do my job properly. My family and friends won't love me. Let's face it, for everybody's sake I have got to start smoking again. I am a confirmed smoker and there is no way I will ever be happy again without a cigarette. (This one kept me smoking for thirty-three years.)

At this stage the smoker usually gives in. He lights a cigarette and the schizophrenia increases. On the one hand there is the tremendous relief of ending the craving, when the little monster finally gets his fix; on the other hand, if he has survived a long time, the cigarette tastes awful and the smoker cannot understand why he is smoking it. This is why the smoker thinks he lacks willpower. In fact, it is not lack of willpower; all he has done is to change his mind and make a perfectly rational decision in the light of the latest information. What's the point of being healthy if you are miserable? What is the point of being rich if you are miserable? Absolutely none. Far better to have a shorter enjoyable life than a lengthy miserable life.'

Fortunately, that is not true – just the reverse. Life as a non-smoker is infinitely more enjoyable, but it was this delusion that kept me smoking for thirty-three years, and I must confess, if that were the true situation, I would still be smoking (correction – I wouldn't be here).

The misery that the smoker is suffering has nothing to do with withdrawal pangs. True, they trigger them off, but the actual agony is in the mind and it is caused by doubt and uncertainty. Because the smoker starts by feeling he is making a sacrifice, he begins to feel deprived – this is a form of stress. One of the times when his brain tells him, 'Have a cigarette,' is a time of stress. Therefore as soon as he stops, he wants a cigarette. But now he can't have one because he has stopped smoking. This makes him more depressed, which sets the trigger off again.

Another thing that makes it so difficult is the waiting for something to happen. If your object is to pass a driving test, as soon as you have passed the test it is certain you have achieved your object. Under the Willpower Method you say, 'If I can go long enough without a cigarette, the urge to smoke will eventually go.'

How do you know when you have achieved it? The answer is that your never do because you are waiting for something to happen and nothing else is going to happen. You stopped when you smoked that last cigarette, and what you are really doing now is waiting to see how long it will be before you give in.

As I said above, the agony that the smoker undergoes is mental, caused by the uncertainty. Although there is no physical pain, it still has a powerful effect. The smoker is miserable and feeling insecure. Far from forgetting about smoking his mind becomes obsessed with it.

There can be days or even weeks of black depression. His mind is obsessed with doubts and fears.

'How long will the craving last?'

'Will I ever be happy again?'

'Will I ever want to get up in the morning?'

'Will I ever enjoy a meal again?'

'How will I ever cope with stress in future?'

'Will I ever enjoy a social function again?'

The smoker is waiting for things to improve, but of course while he is still moping, the cigarette is becoming more precious.

In fact, something does happen, but the smoker isn't conscious of it. If he can survive three weeks without inhaling any nicotine at all, the physical craving for nicotine disappears. However, as stated before, the pangs of withdrawal from nicotine are so mild that the smoker isn't aware of them. But after about three weeks many smokers sense that they have 'kicked it'. They then light a cigarette to prove it, and it does just that. It tastes awful, but the ex-smoker has now supplied nicotine to the body, and as soon as he extinguishes that cigarette the nicotine starts to leave the body. There is now a little voice at the back of his mind saying, 'You want another one.' In fact, he had kicked it but now he has hooked himself again.

The smoker will not usually light another cigarette immediately. He thinks, 'I don't want to get hooked again.' So he allows a safe period to pass. It might be hours, days, even weeks. The ex-smoker can now say, 'Well, I didn't get hooked, so I can safely have another.' He has fallen into the same trap as he did in the first place and is already on the slippery slope.

Smokers who succeed under the Willpower Method tend to find it long and difficult because the main problem is the brainwashing, and long after the physical addiction has died the smoker is still moping about cigarettes. Eventually, if he can survive long enough, it begins to dawn on him that he is not going to give in. He stops moping and accepts that life goes on and is enjoyable without the cigarette.

Many smokers are succeeding with this method, but it is difficult and arduous, and there are many more failures than successes. Even those who do succeed go through the rest of their lives in a vulnerable state. They are left with a certain amount of the brainwashing and believe that during good and bad times the cigarette can give you a boost. (Most non-smokers also suffer from that illusion. They are subjected to the brainwashing also but either find they cannot learn to 'enjoy' smoking or don't want the bad side, thank you very much.) This explains why many smokers who have stopped for long periods start smoking again.

Many ex-smokers will have the occasional cigar or cigarette either as a 'special treat' or to convince themselves how awful they are. It does exactly that, but as soon as they put it out the nicotine starts to leave and a little voice at the back of their mind is saying, 'You want another one.' If they light another one, it still tastes awful and they say, 'Marvellous! While I am not enjoying them I won't get hooked. After Christmas/the holidaday/this trauma, I will stop.'

Too late. They are already hooked. The trap that they fell into in the first place has claimed its victim again.

As I keep saying, enjoyment doesn't come into it. It never did! If we smoked because we enjoyed it, nobody would ever smoke more than one cigarette. We assume we enjoy them only because we cannot believe we would be so stupid as to smoke if we didn't enjoy them. This is why so much of our smoking is subconscious. If, while smoking every cigarette, you were aware of the foul fumes going into your lungs and you had to say to yourself, 'This is going to cost $60,000 in my lifetime, and this cigarette might just be the one to trigger off cancer in my lungs,' even the illusion of enjoyment would go. When we try to block our minds to the bad side, we feel stupid. If we had to face up to it, that would be intolerable! If you watch smokers, particularly at social functions, you will see that they are happy only when they are not aware that they are smoking. Once they become aware of it, they tend to be uncomfortable and apologetic. We smoke to feed that little monster . . . and once you have purged the little monster from your body and the big monster from your brain, you will have neither need nor desire to smoke.

23

Beware of Cutting Down

Many smokers resort to cutting down either as a stepping-stone towards stopping or as an attempt to control the little monster, and many doctors and advisers recommend cutting down as an aid.

Obviously, the less you smoke the better off you are, but, as a stepping-stone to stopping, cutting down is fatal. It is our attempts to cut down that keep us trapped all our lives.

Usually cutting down follows failed attempts to stop. After a few hours or days of abstinence the smoker says to himself something like, 'I cannot face the thought of being without a cigarette, so from now on I will just smoke the special ones or I will cut down to ten a day. If I can get in the habit of smoking ten a day, I can either hold it there or cut down further.'

Certain terrible things now happen.

1 He has the worst of all worlds. He is still addicted to nicotine and is keeping the monster alive not only in his body but also in his mind.
2 He is now wishing his life away waiting for the next cigarette.
3 Prior to cutting down, whenever he wanted a cigarette he lit one up and at least partially relieved his withdrawal pangs. Now, in addition to the normal stresses and strains of life, he is actually causing himself to suffer the withdrawal pangs from nicotine most of his life. So he is causing himself to be miserable and bad tempered.
4 While he was indulging himself, he didn't enjoy most of the cigarettes and he didn't realize he was smoking them. It was automatic. The only cigarettes that he imagined he enjoyed were after a period of abstinence (e.g. the first in the morning, the one after a meal, etc.).

Now that he waits an extra hour for each cigarette, he 'enjoys' every one. The longer he waits, the more enjoyable each cigarette appears to become because the 'enjoyment' in a cigarette isn't the cigarette itself; it's the ending of the agitation caused by the craving, whether it be the slight physical craving for nicotine or the mental moping. The longer you suffer, the more 'enjoyable' each cigarette becomes.

The main difficulty of giving up smoking is not the chemical addiction. That's easy. Smokers will go all night without a cigarette; the craving doesn't even wake them up. Many smokers will actually leave the bedroom before they light up. Many will actually have breakfast. Some will even wait until they arrive at work.

They will go ten hours without a cigarette and it doesn't bother them. If they went ten hours during the day without one, they would be tearing their hair out.

Many smokers will buy a new car and abstain from smoking in it. Smokers will visit supermarkets, theatres, doctors, hospitals, dentists and so on without undue inconvenience. Many smokers will abstain in the company of non-smokers. Even on the Tube trains there have been no riots. Smokers are almost pleased for someone to say they cannot smoke. In fact, smokers get a secret pleasure out of going long periods without a cigarette. It gives them the hope that maybe one day they will never want another one.

The real problem of giving up smoking is the brainwashing, the illusion that the cigarette is some sort of prop or reward and life will never be quite the same without it. Far from turning you off smoking, all cutting down does is to leave you feeling insecure and miserable and to convince you that the most precious thing on this earth is the next cigarette, that there is no way that you will ever be happy again without one.

There is nothing more pathetic than the smoker who is trying to cut down. He suffers from the delusion that the less he smokes, the less he will want to smoke. In fact, the reverse is true. The less he smokes, the longer he suffers the withdrawal pangs; the more he enjoys the cigarette, the more distasteful they become. But that won't stop him smoking. Taste never, ever came into it. If smokers smoked because they enjoyed the taste, nobody would ever smoke more than one cigarette. You find that difficult to believe? OK, let's talk it out. Which is the worst-tasting cigarette? That's right, the first in the morning, the one that in winter sets us coughing and spluttering. Which is one of the most precious cigarettes for most smokers? That's right, the first cigarette in the morning! Now do you really believe you are smoking it to enjoy the taste and smell, or do you think a more rational explanation is that you are relieving nine hours' withdrawal pangs?

Cutting down not only doesn't work but it is the worst form of torture. It doesn't work because initially the smoker hopes that by getting into the habit of smoking less and less, he will reduce his desire to smoke a cigarette. It is not a habit. It is an addiction, and the nature of any addiction is to want more and more, not less and less. Therefore in order to cut down, the smoker has to exercise willpower and discipline for the rest of his life.

The main problem of stopping smoking is not the chemical addiction to nicotine. That's easy to cope with. It is the mistaken belief that the cigarette gives you some pleasure. This mistaken belief is brought about initially by the brainwashing we receive before we start smoking, which is then reinforced by the actual addiction. All cutting down does is to reinforce the fallacy further to the extent that smoking dominates the smoker's life completely and convinces him that the most precious thing on this earth is the next cigarette.

As I have already said, cutting down never works anyway because you have to exercise willpower and discipline for the rest of your life. If you had not enough willpower to stop, then you certainly have not got enough to cut down. Stopping is far easier and less painful.

I have heard of literally thousands of cases in which cutting down has failed. The handful of successes I have known have been achieved after a relatively short period of cutting down, followed by the 'cold turkey'. The smokers really stopped in spite of cutting down, not because of it. All it did was to prolong the agony. A failed attempt to cut down leaves the smoker a nervous wreck, even more convinced that he is hooked for life. This is usually enough to keep him puffing away for another five years before the next attempt.

However, cutting down helps to illustrate the whole futility of the smoking habit because it clearly illustrates that a cigarette is enjoyable only after a period of abstinence. You have to bang your head against a brick wall (i.e. suffer withdrawal pangs) to make it nice when you stop.

So the choice is:

1 Cut down for life. This will be self-imposed torture, and you will not be able to do it anyway.

2 Increasingly choke yourself for life. What is the point?

3 Be nice to yourself. Give it up.

The other important point that cutting down demonstrates is that there is no such thing as the odd cigarette, the occasional cigarette. Smoking is a chain reaction that will last the rest of your life unless you make a positive effort to break it.

REMEMBER: CUTTING DOWN WILL DRAG YOU DOWN.

24

Just One Cigarette

'Just one cigarette' is a myth you must get out of your mind.

It is just one cigarette that gets us started in the first place.

It is just one cigarette to tide us over a difficult patch or on a special occasion that defeats most of our attempts to stop.

It is just one cigarette that, when smokers have succeeded in breaking the addiction, sends them back into the trap. Sometimes it is just to confirm that they do not need them any more, and that one cigarette does just that. It tastes horrible and convinces the smoker he will never become hooked again, but he already is.

It is the thought of that one special cigarette that often prevents smokers from stopping. The first one in the morning or the one after a meal.

Get it firmly in your mind there is no such thing as just one cigarette. It is a chain reaction that will last the rest of your life unless you break it.

It is the myth about the odd, special cigarette that keeps smokers moping about it when they stop. Get into the habit of never seeing the odd cigarette or packet – it is a fantasy. Whenever you think about smoking, see a whole filthy lifetime of spending a small fortune just for the privilege of destroying yourself mentally and physically, a lifetime of slavery, a lifetime of bad breath.

It is a pity that there isn't something like a cigarette that, during good and bad times, we can use for an occasional boost or pleasure. But get it clearly into your mind: the cigarette isn't it. You are stuck with either a lifetime of misery or none at all. You wouldn't dream of taking cyanide because you liked the taste of almonds, so stop punishing yourself with the thought of the occasional cigarette or cigar.

Ask a smoker, 'If you had the opportunity to go back to the time before you became hooked, would you have become a smoker?' The answer is inevitably 'You have got to be joking', yet every

70

smoker has that choice every day of his life. Why doesn't he opt for it? The answer is fear. The fear that he cannot stop or that life won't be the same without it.

Stop kidding yourself. You can do it. Anybody can. It's ridiculously easy.

In order to make it easy to stop smoking there are certain fundamentals to get clear in your mind. We have already dealt with three of them up to now:

1 There is nothing to give up. There are only marvellous positive gains to achieve.
2 Never see the odd cigarette. It doesn't exist. There is only a lifetime of filth and disease.
3 There is nothing different about you. Any smoker can find it easy to stop.

25

Casual Smokers, Teenagers, Non-smokers

Heavy smokers tend to envy the casual smoker. Don't. In a peculiar way, the casual smoker is more hooked and miserable than the heavy smoker. It is true that he is less vulnerable to the fearful physical risks to his health and that he is not spending as much money as you. However, in other ways he is far worse off.

Remember, no smoker actually enjoys cigarettes. All he enjoys is relieving withdrawal pangs. The natural tendency of the drug is to relieve withdrawal pangs. Therefore the natural tendency is to chain-smoke.

There are three main factors that prevent smokers from chain-smoking.

1 MONEY. Most cannot afford to.
2 HEALTH. In order to relieve our withdrawal pangs, we have to take a poisonous product. Capacity to cope with that poison varies with each individual and at different times and situations in his or her life. This acts as an automatic restraint.
3 DISCIPLINE. This is imposed by society, or the smoker's job, or friends and relatives, or by the smoker himself as a result of the natural tug of war that goes on in every smoker's mind.

It may be of advantage at this stage to provide a few definitions.

THE NON-SMOKER. Someone who has never fallen for the trap but should not be complacent. He is a non-smoker only by the grace of God. All smokers were convinced that they would never become hooked, and some non-smokers keep trying that occasional cigarette.

THE CASUAL SMOKER. There are two basic classifications of casual smokers.

1 The smoker who has fallen for the trap but doesn't realize it. Do not envy such smokers. They are merely on the first rung of the ladder and in all probability will soon be heavy smokers. Remember, you started off as a casual smoker.
2 The smoker who was previously a heavy smoker and thinks he cannot stop. These smokers are the most pathetic of all. They fall into various categories, each of which needs separate comment.

THE FIVE-A-DAY SMOKER. If he enjoys a cigarette, why does he smoke only five a day? If he can take it or leave it, why does he bother to smoke at all? Remember, the habit is really banging your head against the brick wall to make it relaxing when you stop. The five-a-day smoker is relieving his withdrawal pangs for less than one hour each day. The rest of the day, although he doesn't realize it, he is banging his head against the wall and does so for most of his life. He is smoking only five a day because either he cannot afford to smoke more or he is worried about the health risk. It is easy to convince the heavy smoker that he doesn't enjoy it, but you try convincing a casual smoker. Anybody who has gone through an attempt to cut down will know it is the worst torture of all and almost guaranteed to keep you hooked the rest of your life.

THE MORNING- OR EVENING-ONLY SMOKER. He punishes himself by suffering withdrawal pangs for half the day in order to relieve them the other half. Again, ask him why, if he enjoys a cigarette, he doesn't smoke the whole day or, if he doesn't enjoy a cigarette, he bothers at all.

THE SIX-MONTHS-ON, SIX-MONTHS-OFF SMOKER. (Or 'I can stop whenever I want to. I have done it thousands of times.') If he enjoys smoking, why does he stop for six months? If he does not enjoy it, why does he start again? The truth is he is still hooked. Although he gets rid of the physical addiction, he is left with the main problem – the brainwashing. He hopes each time that he will stop for good and soon falls for the trap again. Many smokers envy these stoppers and starters. They think, 'How lucky to be able to control it like that, to smoke when you want to and stop when you want to.' What they always overlook is that these stoppers and starters aren't controlling it. When they are smokers, they wish they weren't. Then they go through the hassle of stopping, then

73

begin to feel deprived and fall for the trap again, then wish they hadn't. They get the worst of all worlds. When they are smokers they wish they weren't; when they are non-smokers they wish they could smoke. If you think about it, this is true all our smoking lives. When we are allowed to smoke we either take it for granted or wish we didn't. It's only when we can't have cigarettes that they appear so precious. This is the awful dilemma of smokers. They can never win because they are moping over a myth, an illusion. There is one way they can win and that is to stop smoking *and* stop moping!

THE 'I ONLY SMOKE ON SPECIAL OCCASIONS' SMOKER. Yes, we all do to start with, but isn't it amazing how the number of occasions seem rapidly to increase and before we know it we seem to be smoking on all occasions?

THE 'I HAVE STOPPED BUT I HAVE AN OCCASIONAL CIGAR/ CIGARETTE' SMOKER. In a way such smokers are the most pathetic of all. Either they go through their lives believing they are being deprived or, more often, the occasional cigar becomes two. They remain on the slippery slope and it goes only one way – DOWNWARDS. Sooner or later they are back to being heavy smokers. They have fallen for the very trap that they fell into in the first place.

There are two other categories of casual smoker. The first is the type who smokes just the occasional cigarette or cigar at social occasions. These people are really non-smokers. They don't enjoy smoking. It's just that they feel they are missing out. They want to be part of the action. We all start off like this. Next time the cigars go round, watch how, after a while, the smokers stop lighting those cigars. Even heavy cigarette smokers can't wait to finish them. They would much rather be smoking their own brand. The more expensive and the larger the cigar, the more frustrating it is – the damn thing seems to last all night.

The second category is very rare indeed. In fact, of all the thousands who have sought my assistance, I can think of only about a dozen examples. The type can best be described by outlining a recent case.

A woman phoned me, seeking a private session. She is a solicitor, had been smoking for about twelve years and had never smoked more or less than two cigarettes a day in her smoking life. She was, incidentally, a very strong-willed lady. I explained that the success rate in group sessions was greater than in individual sessions, and in any event I was able to give individual therapy only if the face were so famous that it would disrupt the group. She began to cry, and I was not able to resist the tears.

The session was expensive; indeed, most smokers would wonder why she wanted to stop in the first place. They would gladly pay what I charged that lady to be able to smoke only two cigarettes a day. They make the mistake of assuming that casual smokers are happier and more in control. In control they may be, but happy they are not. In this case, both the woman's parents had died from lung cancer before she became hooked. Like me, she had a great fear of smoking before she smoked the first cigarette. Like me, she eventually fell victim to the massive pressures and tried that first cigarette. Like me, she can remember the foul taste. Unlike me, who capitulated and became a chain-smoker very quickly, she resisted the slide.

All you ever enjoy in a cigarette is the ending of the craving for it, whether it be the almost imperceptible physical craving for nicotine or the mental torture caused by not being allowed to scratch the itch. Cigarettes themselves are filth and poison. This is why you only suffer the illusion of enjoying them after a period of abstinence. Just like a hunger or thirst, the longer you suffer it, the greater of the pleasure when you finally relieve it. Smokers make the mistake of believing smoking is just a habit. They think, 'If I can only keep it down to a certain level or smoke only on special occasions, my brain and body will accept it. I can then keep my smoking at that level or cut down further should I wish to.' Get it clear in your mind: the 'habit' doesn't exist. Smoking is drug addiction. The natural tendency is to relieve withdrawal pangs, not to endure them. Even to hold it at the level you are already at, you would have to exercise willpower and discipline the rest of your life because, as your body becomes immune to the drug, it wants more and more, not less and less. As the drug begins to destroy you physically and mentally, as it gradually breaks down your nervous system, your courage and confidence, so you are increasingly unable to resist reducing the interval between each cigarette. That is why, in the early days, we can take it or leave it. If we get a cold, we just stop. It also explains why someone like me, who never even suffered the illusion of enjoying them, had to go on chain-smoking even though every cigarette had become physical torture.

Don't envy that woman. When you smoke only one cigarette every twelve hours it appears to be the most precious thing on earth. For twelve years that poor woman had been at the centre of a tug of war. She had been unable to stop smoking, yet was frightened to increase the intake in case she got lung cancer like her parents. But for twenty-three hours and ten minutes of every one of those days she had to fight the temptation. It took tremendous willpower to do what she did, and, as I have said, such cases are rare. But it reduced her to tears in the end. Just look at it logically: either there is a genuine crutch or pleasure in smoking or there isn't. If there is, who wants to wait an hour, or a day, or a week? Why should you be denied the crutch or pleasure in the meantime? If there is no genuine crutch or pleasure, why bother to smoke any of them?

I remember another case, that of a five-a-day man. He started the telephone conversation in a croaky voice: 'Mr Carr, I just want to stop smoking before I die.' This is how that man described his life.

'I am sixty-one years old. I have got cancer of the throat through smoking. Now I can only physically cope with five roll-ups a day.

'I used to sleep soundly through the night. Now I wake up every hour of the night and all I can think about is cigarettes. Even when I am sleeping, I dream about smoking.

'I cannot smoke my first cigarette until 10 o'clock. I get up at 5 o'clock and make endless cups of tea. My wife gets up at about 8 o'clock and, because I am so bad-tempered, she will not have me in the house. I go down to the greenhouse and try to potter about, but my mind is obsessed with smoking. At 9 o'clock I begin to roll my first cigarette and I do so until it is perfect. It is not that I need it to be perfect, but it gives me something to do. I then wait for 10 o'clock. When it arrives my hands are shaking uncontrollably. I do not light the cigarette then. If I do, I have to wait three hours for the next one. Eventually I light the cigarette, take one puff and extinguish it immediately. By continuing this process I can make the cigarette last one hour. I smoke it down to about a quarter of an inch and then wait for the next one.'

In addition to his other troubles, this poor man had burns all over his lips caused by smoking the cigarette too low. You probably have visions of a pathetic imbecile. Not so. This man was over six feet tall and an ex-sergeant in the Marines. He was a former athlete and didn't want to become a smoker. However, in the last war society believed that cigarettes gave courage, and servicemen

76

were issued free rations of them. This man was virtually ordered to become a smoker. He has spent the rest of his life paying through the nose, subsidizing other people's taxes, and it has ruined him physically and mentally. If he were an animal, our society would have put him out of his misery, yet we still allow mentally and physically healthy young teenagers to become hooked.

You may think the above case is exaggerated. It is extreme but not unique. There are literally thousands of similar stories. That man poured his heart out to me, but you can be sure that many of his friends and acquaintances envied him for being a five-a-day man. If you think this couldn't happen to you, STOP KIDDING YOURSELF.

IT IS ALREADY HAPPENING.

In any event smokers are notorious liars, even to themselves. They have to be. Most casual smokers smoke far more cigarettes, and on far more occasions, than they will admit to. I have had many conversations with so-called five-a-day smokers during which they have smoked more than five cigarettes in my presence. Observe casual smokers at social events such as weddings and parties. They will be chain-smoking like the best of them.

You do not need to envy casual smokers. You do not need to smoke. Life is infinitely sweeter without cigarettes.

Teenagers are generally more difficult to cure, not because they find it difficult to stop but because either they do not believe they are hooked or they are at the primary stage of the disease and suffer from the delusion that they will automatically have stopped before the secondary stage.

I would like particularly to warn parents of children who loathe smoking not to have a false sense of security. All children loathe the smell and taste of tobacco until they become hooked. You did too at one time. Also do not be fooled by government scare campaigns. The trap is the same as it always was. Children know that cigarettes kill, but they also know that one cigarette will not do it. At some stage they may be influenced by a girlfriend or boyfriend, schoolfriend or work colleague. You may think that all they need is to try one, which will taste horrible and convince them they could never become hooked. *Warn your children of the full facts.*

26

The Secret Smoker

The secret smoker should be grouped with casual smokers, but the effects of secret smoking are so insidious that it merits a separate chapter. It can lead to the breakdown of personal relationships. In my case it nearly caused a divorce.

I was three weeks into one of my failed attempts to stop. The attempt had been triggered off by my wife's worry about my constant wheezing and coughing. I had told her I was not worried about my health. She said, 'I know you are not, but how would you feel if you had to watch someone you love systematically destroying themselves?' It was an argument that I found irresistible, hence the attempt to stop. The attempt ended after three weeks after a heated argument with an old friend. It did not register until years afterwards that my devious mind had deliberately triggered off the argument. I felt justly aggrieved at the time, but I do not believe that it was coincidence, as I had never argued with this particular friend before or since. It was clearly the little monster at work. Anyway, I had my excuse. I desperately needed a cigarette and started smoking again.

I could not bear to think of the disappointment this would cause my wife, so I did not tell her. I just smoked when alone. Then gradually I smoked in the company of friends until it got to the point where everybody knew I was smoking except my wife. I remember being quite pleased at the time. I thought, 'Well, at least it is cutting my consumption down.' Eventually she accused me of continuing to smoke. I had not realized it, but she described the times I had caused an argument and stormed out of the house. At other times I had taken two hours to purchase some minor item, and on occasions when I would normally have invited her to accompany me, I had made feeble excuses to go alone.

As the antisocial split between smokers and non-smokers widens, there are literally thousands of cases where the company of friends or relatives is restricted or avoided because of this awful weed. The worst thing about secret smoking is that it supports the fallacy in the smoker's mind that he is being deprived. At the same time, it causes a major loss of self-respect; an otherwise honest person may force himself to deceive his family and friends.

It has probably happened or is still happening to you in some form.

27

A Social Habit?

The main reason why there are over 10 million ex-smokers in Britain since the 1960s is the social revolution that is taking place.

Yes, I know: health followed by money are the main reasons why we should want to stop, but then they always have been. We do not actually need cancer scares to tell us that cigarettes shatter our lives. These bodies of ours are the most sophisticated objects on the planet, and any smoker knows instantly, from the first puff, that cigarettes are poisonous.

The only reason why we ever get involved with smoking is the social pressure of our friends. The only valid 'plus' smoking ever had was that it was at one time considered a perfectly acceptable social habit.

Today it is generally considered, even by smokers themselves, to be an antisocial habit.

In the old days the strong man smoked. If you didn't smoke, you were considered to be a cissy, and we all worked very hard to become hooked. In every public house or club bar the majority of men would be proudly inhaling and exhaling tobacco smoke. There would be the permanent fall-out cloud, and all the ceilings that were not regularly decorated soon became yellow or brown.

Today the position is completely reversed. Today's strong man doesn't need to smoke. Today's strong man is not dependent on a drug.

With the social revolution all smokers nowadays are giving serious thought to stopping, and today's smokers are considered to be generally weak people.

The most significant trend that I have noticed since writing the first edition of this book in 1985 is the increasing emphasis on the antisocial aspect of smoking. The days when the cigarette was the proud badge of the sophisticated woman or the tough guy have gone for ever. Everyone now knows that the only reason why people continue to smoke is because they have failed to stop or are too frightened to try. Every day as the smoker is pilloried by office bans, extended bans in public places, attacks from holier-than-thou ex-smokers, so the mannerisms of smokers become ever more apparent. I've recently seen situations that I remember as a boy but I haven't seen for years – like smokers flicking ash into their hands or pockets because they are too embarrassed to ask for an ashtray.

I was in a restaurant three Christmases or so ago. It was midnight. Everyone had stopped eating. At a time when the cigarettes and cigars are normally rife, not one person was smoking. I conceitedly thought, 'Ah! I'm beginning to make an impression.' I said to the waiter, 'Is this now a non-smoking restaurant?' The reply was negative. I thought, 'That's strange. I know that a lot of people are stopping, but there must be one smoker here.' Eventually someone lit up in a corner, and the result was like a series of beacons going through the restaurant. All those other smokers had been sitting there thinking, 'Surely I can't be the only smoker here.'

Many smokers won't smoke between courses now because they feel so self-conscious. Many not only apologize to people on the same table but also look around to see if they'll get flak from elsewhere. As every day more and more smokers leave the sinking ship, so those left on it become terrified they'll be the last.

DON'T LET IT BE YOU!

28

Timing

Apart from the obvious point that as it is doing you no good, now is the right time to stop, I believe timing is important. Our society treats smoking flippantly as a slightly distasteful habit that can injure your health. It is not. It is drug addiction, a disease and the No. 1 killer in Western society. The worst thing that happens in most smokers' lives is getting hooked on that awful weed. If they stay hooked, horrendous things happen. Timing is important to give yourself the right to a proper cure.

First of all, identify the times or occasions when smoking appears to be important to you. If you are a businessman and smoke for the illusion of relief of stress, pick a relatively slack period; a good idea is to choose your annual holiday. If you smoke mainly during boring or relaxing periods, do the opposite. In any event take the matter seriously and make the attempt the most important thing in your life.

Look ahead for a period of about three weeks and try to anticipate any event that might lead to failure. Occasions like a wedding or Christmas need not deter you, providing you anticipate them in advance and do not feel you will be deprived. Do not attempt to cut down in the meantime, as this will only create the illusion that the cigarette is enjoyable. In fact, it helps to force as many of the filthy things down your throat as possible. While you are smoking that last cigarette, be conscious of the bad smell and taste and think how marvellous it will be when you allow yourself to stop doing it.

WHATEVER YOU DO, DON'T FALL INTO THE TRAP OF JUST SAYING, 'NOT NOW. LATER,' AND PUTTING IT OUT OF YOUR MIND. WORK OUT YOUR TIMETABLE NOW AND LOOK FORWARD TO IT. Remember you aren't giving anything up. On the contrary: you are about to receive marvellous positive gains.

For years I've been saying I know more about the mysteries of smoking than anyone on this planet. The problem is this: although every smoker smokes purely to relieve the chemical craving for nicotine, it is not the nicotine addiction itself that hooks the smoker but the brainwashing that results from that addiction. An intelligent person will fall for a confidence trick. But only a fool will go on falling for it once he realizes that it's a confidence trick. Fortunately, most smokers aren't fools; they only think they are. Each individual smoker has his own private brainwashing. That is why there appears to be such a wide range of different types of smoker, which only serves to compound the mysteries.

With the benefit of the five years' feedback that I have had since the original publication of this book, and bearing in mind that each day I learn something new about smoking, I was agreeably surprised to realize that the philosophy I propounded in the first edition was still sound. The accumulated knowledge that I have acquired over the years is how to communicate that knowledge to each individual smoker. The fact that I know every smoker could not only find it easy to stop but would actually enjoy the process is not only pointless but exceedingly frustrating unless I can make the smoker realize it.

Many people have said to me, 'You say, "Continue to smoke until you have finished the book." This tends to make the smoker take ages to read the book or just not finish it, period. Therefore you should change that instruction.' This sounds logical, but I know that if the instruction were 'Stop Immediately', some smokers wouldn't even start reading the book.

I had a smoker consult me in the early days. He said, 'I really resent having to seek your help. I know I'm strong-willed. In every other area of my life I'm in control. Why is it that all these other smokers are stopping by using their own willpower, yet I have to come to you?' He continued, 'I think I could do it on my own, if I could smoke while I was doing it.'

This may sound like a contradiction, but I know what the man meant. We think of stopping smoking as something that is very difficult to do. What do we need when we have something difficult to do? We need our little friend. So stopping smoking appears to be a double blow. Not only do we have a difficult task to perform, which is hard enough, but the crutch on which we normally rely on such occasions is no longer available.

It didn't occur to me until long after the man had left that my instruction to keep smoking is the real beauty of my method.

You can continue to smoke while you go through the process of stopping. You get rid of all your doubts and fears first, and when you extinguish that final cigarette you are already a non-smoker and enjoying being one.

The only chapter that has caused me to question my original advice seriously is this chapter on the matter of the right timing. Above I advise that if your special cigarette occasions are stress situations at the office, then pick a holiday to make an attempt to give up, and vice versa. In fact, that isn't the easiest way to do it. The easiest way is to pick what you consider to be the most *difficult* time to do it, whether it be stress, social, concentration or boredom. Once you've proved that you can cope with, and enjoy, life in the worst possible situation, every other situation becomes easy. But if I gave that as a definite instruction, would you even make the attempt to stop?

Let me use an analogy. My wife and I intend to swim together. We arrive at the pool at the same time, but we rarely swim together. The reason is that she immerses one toe, and half an hour later she's actually swimming. I cannot stand that slow torture. I know in advance that at some stage, no matter how cold the water is, eventually I'm going to have to brave it. So I've learned to do it the easy way: I dive straight in. Now, assuming that I were in a position to insist that if she didn't dive straight in, she couldn't swim at all, I know that she wouldn't swim at all. You see the problem.

From feedback I know that many smokers have used the original advice I gave on timing to delay what they think will be the evil day. My next thoughts were to use the technique that I used for the chapter on the advantages of smoking, something like: 'timing is very important, and in the next chapter I will advise you about the best time for you to make the attempt.' You turn the page over, and there is just a huge NOW. That is, in fact, the best advice, but would you take it?

This is the most subtle aspect of the smoking trap. When we have genuine stress in our lives, it's not the time to stop, and if we have no stress in our lives, we have no desire to stop.

Ask yourself these following questions.

When you smoked that very first cigarette, did you really decide then that you would continue to smoke the rest of your life, all day, every day, without ever being able to stop?

OF COURSE YOU DIDN'T!

84

Are you going to continue the rest of your life all day, every day, without ever being able to stop?

OF COURSE YOU AREN'T!

So when will you stop? Tomorrow? Next year? The year after?

Isn't this what you've been asking yourself since you first realized you were hooked? Are you hoping that one morning you will wake up and just not want to smoke any more? Stop kidding yourself. I waited thirty-three years for it to happen to me. With drug addiction you get progressively more hooked, not less. You think it will be easier tomorrow? You're still kidding yourself. If you can't do it today, what makes you think it will be easier tomorrow? Are you going to wait until you've actually contracted one of the killer diseases? That would be a bit pointless.

The real trap is the belief that now isn't the right time – it will always be easier tomorrow.

We believe that we live stressful lives. In fact, we don't. We've taken most genuine stress out of our lives. When you leave your home you don't live in fear of being attacked by wild animals. Most of us don't have to worry where our next meal is coming from, or whether we'll have a roof over our head tonight. But just think of the life of a wild animal. Every time a rabbit comes out of its burrow, it is facing Vietnam the whole of its life. But the rabbit can handle it. It's got adrenalin and other hormones – and so have we. The truth is, the most stressful periods for any creature are early childhood and adolescence. But 3 billion years of natural selection have equipped us to cope with stress. I was five years old when the war started. We were bombed out, and I was separated from my parents for two years. I was billeted with people who treated me unkindly. It was an unpleasant period in my life, but I was able to cope with it. I don't believe it has left me with any permanent scars; on the contrary, I believe it has made me a stronger person. When I look back on my life there has only been one thing that I couldn't handle and that was my slavery to that damned weed.

A few years ago I thought I had all the worries in the world. I was suicidal – not in the sense that I would have jumped off a roof but in the sense that I knew that smoking would soon kill me. I argued that if this was life with my crutch, life just wouldn't be worth living without it. What I didn't realize was that when you are physically and mentally depressed everything gets you down.

85

Now I feel like a young boy again. Only one thing made the change in my life: I'm now out of the smoking pit.

I know it's a cliché to say, 'If you haven't got your health, you've got nothing,' but it's absolutely true. I used to think that physical-fitness fanatics like Gary Player were a pain. I used to claim there's more to life than feeling fit; there's booze and tobacco. That's nonsense. When you feel physically and mentally strong you can enjoy the highs and handle the lows. We confuse responsibility with stress. Responsibility becomes stressful only when you don't feel strong enough to handle it. The Richard Burtons of this world are physically and mentally strong. What destroys them is not the stresses of life, or their jobs, or old age but the so-called crutches they turn to, which are just illusions. Sadly, in his case and for millions like him, the crutches kill.

Look at it this way. You've already decided that you are not going to stay in the trap the rest of your life. Therefore at some time in your life, whether you find it easy or difficult, you will have to go through the process of getting free. Smoking is not a habit or pleasure. It is drug addiction and a disease. We've already established that, far from being easier to stop tomorrow, it will get progressively harder. With a disease that's going to get progressively worse, the time to get rid of it is NOW – or as near to now as you can manage. Just think how quickly each week of our lives comes and goes. That's all it takes. Just think how nice it will be to enjoy the rest of your life without that ever-increasing black shadow hanging over you. And if you follow all my instructions, you won't even have to wait five days. You won't simply find it easy after extinguishing the final cigarette: YOU'LL ENJOY IT!

29

Will I Miss the Cigarette?

No! Once that little nicotine monster is dead and your body stops craving nicotine, any remaining brainwashing will vanish and you will find that you will be both physically and mentally better equipped not only to cope with the stresses and strains of life but to enjoy the good times to the full.

There is only one danger and that is the influence of people who are still smoking. 'The other man's grass is always greener' is a commonplace in many aspects of our lives and is easily understandable. Why is it in the case of smoking, where the disadvantages are so enormous as compared with even the illusory 'advantages', that ex-smokers tend to envy the smoker?

With all the brainwashing of our childhood it is quite understandable that we fall into the trap. Why is it that, once we realize what a mug's game it is and many of us manage to kick the habit, we walk straight back into the same trap? It is the influence of smokers.

It usually happens on social occasions, particularly after a meal. The smoker lights up and the ex-smoker has a pang. This is indeed a curious anomaly, particularly if you consider this piece of market research: not only is every non-smoker in the world happy to be a non-smoker but every smoker in the world, even with his warped, addicted, brainwashed mind suffering the delusion that he enjoys it or it relaxes him, wishes he had never become hooked in the first place. So why do some ex-smokers envy the smoker on these occasions? There are two reasons.

1 'Just one cigarette.' Remember: it doesn't exist. Stop seeing that isolated occasion and start looking at it from the point of view of the smoker. You may be envying him, but he doesn't approve of himself; he envies you. Start observing other smokers. They can be the most powerful boost of all to help you off

it. Notice how quickly the cigarette burns, how quickly the smoker has to light up another. Notice particularly that not only is he not aware that he is smoking the cigarette but even the lighting up appears to be automatic. Remember, he is not enjoying it; it's just that he cannot enjoy himself without it. Particularly remember that when he leaves your company he is going to have to go on smoking. The next morning, when he wakes up with a chest like a cesspit, he is going to have to carry on choking himself. The next Budget Day, the next time he has a pain in the chest, the next National No-Smoking Day, the next time he inadvertently sees the government health warning, the next time there is a cancer scare, the next time he is in church, on a train, visiting a hospital, library, dentist, doctor, supermarket, etc., the next time he is in the company of a non-smoker, he has to continue this lifetime chain of paying through the nose just for the privilege of destroying himself physically and mentally. He is facing a lifetime of filth, bad breath, stained teeth, a lifetime of slavery, a lifetime of destroying himself, a lifetime of black shadows at the back of his mind. All of this is to achieve what purpose? The illusion of trying to get back to the state he was in before he became hooked in the first place.

2 The second reason why some ex-smokers have pangs on these occasions is because the smoker is doing something, i.e. smoking a cigarette, and the non-smoker is not, so he tends to feel deprived. Get it clear in your mind before you start: it is not the non-smoker who is being deprived. It is the poor smoker who is being deprived of

HEALTH
ENERGY
MONEY
CONFIDENCE
PEACE OF MIND
COURAGE
TRANQUILLITY
FREEDOM
SELF-RESPECT.

Get out of the habit of envying smokers and start seeing them as the miserable, pathetic creatures they really are. I know: I was the world's worst. That is why you are reading this book, and the ones who cannot face up to it, who have to go on kidding themselves, are the most pathetic of all.

You wouldn't envy a heroin addict. Heroin kills fewer than 300 people a year in this country. Nicotine kills over 100,000 a year and 2.5 million a year world-wide. It's already killed more people on this planet than all the wars of history combined. Like all drug addiction, yours won't get better. Each year it will get worse and worse. If you don't enjoy being a smoker today, you'll enjoy it even less tomorrow. Don't envy other smokers. Pity them. Believe me: THEY NEED YOUR PITY.

30

Will I Put on Weight?

This is another myth about smoking, spread mainly by smokers who, when attempting to stop under the Willpower Method, substitute sweets, etc., to help relieve withdrawal pangs. The withdrawal pangs of nicotine are very similar to hunger pangs, and the two are easily confused. However, whereas the pangs of hunger can be satisfied by food, the withdrawal pangs of nicotine are never completely satisfied.

As with any drug, after a while the body becomes immune and the drug ceases to relieve the withdrawal pangs completely. As soon as we extinguish a cigarette, the nicotine rapidly leaves our body, so that the nicotine addict has a permanent hunger. The natural inclination is eventually to chain-smoke. However, most smokers are prevented from doing this for one, or both, of two reasons.

1 Money – they cannot afford to increase their intake.
2 Health – in order to relieve the withdrawal pangs we have to intake a poison, which acts as an automatic check on the number of cigarettes we can smoke.

The smoker is therefore left with a permanent hunger that he can never satisfy. This is why many smokers turn to over-eating, heavy drinking or even harder drugs in order to satisfy the void. (MOST ALCOHOLICS ARE HEAVY SMOKERS. I WONDER IF IT IS REALLY A SMOKING PROBLEM?)

For the smoker the normal tendency is to start by substituting nicotine for food. During my own nightmare years I got to the stage where I cut out breakfast and lunch completely. I would chain-smoke during the day. In the later years I would actually look forward to the evenings only because then I could stop smoking. However, I would be picking at food all evening. I thought it was hunger, but it was really the withdrawal pangs from nicotine. In other words, during the day I would substitute nicotine for food and during the evenings I would substitute food for nicotine.

In those days I was two stone heavier than I am now and there was nothing I could do about it.

Once that little monster leaves your body, the awful feeling of insecurity ends. Your confidence returns, together with a marvellous feeling of self-respect. You obtain the assurance to take control of your life, not only in your eating habits but also in all other ways. This is one of the many great advantages of being free from the weed.

As I have said, the weight myth is due to using substitutes during the withdrawal period. In fact, they do not make it easier to stop. They make it harder. This is explained in greater detail in a later chapter dealing with substitutes.

31

Avoid False Incentives

Many smokers, while trying to stop under the Willpower Method, try to increase the incentive to stop by building up false incentives.

There are many examples of this. A typical one is 'My family and I can have a marvellous holiday on the money I will save.' This appears to be a logical and sensible approach, but in fact it is false because any self-respecting smoker would rather smoke fifty-two weeks in the year and not have a holiday. In any case there is a doubt in the smoker's mind because not only will he have to abstain for fifty weeks but will he even enjoy that holiday without a cigarette? All this does is to increase the sacrifice that the smoker feels he is making, which makes the cigarette even more precious in his mind. Instead concentrate on the other side: 'What am I getting out of it? Why do I need to smoke?' Another example: 'I'll be able to afford a better car.' That's true, and the incentive may make you abstain until you get that car, but once the novelty has gone you will feel deprived, and sooner or later you will fall for the trap again.

Another typical example is office or family pacts. These have the advantage of eliminating temptation for certain periods of the day. However, they generally fail for the following reasons.

1 The incentive is false. Why should you want to stop smoking just because other people are doing so? All this does is to create an additional pressure, which increases the element of sacrifice. It is fine if all smokers genuinely want to stop at one particular time. However, you cannot force smokers to stop, and although all smokers secretly want to, until they are ready to do so a pact just creates additional pressure, which increases their desire to smoke. This turns them into secret smokers, which further increases the feeling of dependency.

2 The 'Rotten apple' theory, or dependency on each other. Under the Willpower Method of stopping, the smoker is undergoing a period of penance during which he waits for the urge to smoke to go. If he gives in, there is a sense of failure. Under the Willpower Method one of the participants is bound to give in sooner or later. The other participants now have the excuse they have been waiting for. It's not their fault. They would have held out. It is just that Fred has let them down. The truth is that most of them have already been cheating.

3 'Sharing the credit' is the reverse of the 'Rotten apple' theory. Here the loss of face due to failure is not so bad when shared. There is a marvellous sense of achievement in stopping smoking. When you are doing it alone the acclaim you receive from your friends, relatives and colleagues can be a tremendous boost to help you over the first few days. When everybody is doing it at the same time the credit has to be shared and the boost is consequently reduced.

Another classic example of false incentives is the bribe (e.g. the parent offering the teenager a sum of money to abstain or the bet, 'I will give you $200 if I fail'). There was once an example in a TV programme. A policeman trying to give up smoking put a $50 note in his cigarette packet. He had a pact with himself. He could smoke again, but he had to set light first to the $50 note. This stopped him for a few days, but eventually he burnt the note.

Stop kidding yourself. If the $60,000 that the average smoker spends in his life won't stop him, or the one-in-four risk of horrendous diseases, or the lifetime of bad breath, mental and physical torture and slavery or being despised by most of the population and despising yourself, a few phoney incentives will not make the slightest bit of difference. They will only make the sacrifice appear worse. Keep looking at the other side of the tug of war.

What is smoking doing for me? ABSOLUTELY NOTHING.

Why do I need to do it? YOU DON'T! YOU ARE ONLY PUNISHING YOURSELF.

32

The Easy Way to Stop

This chapter contains instructions about the easy way to stop smoking. Providing you follow the instructions, you will find that stopping ranges from relatively easy to enjoyable! But remember the definition of a brunette: 'a girl who didn't read the instructions on the bottle'.

It is ridiculously easy to stop smoking. All you have to do is two things.

1 Make the decision that you are never going to smoke again.
2 Don't mope about it. Rejoice.

You are probably asking, 'Why the need for the rest of the book? Why couldn't you have said that in the first place?' The answer is that you would at some time have moped about it, and consequently, sooner or later, you would have changed your decision. You have probably already done it many times before.

As I have already said, the whole business of smoking is a subtle, sinister trap. The main problem of stopping isn't the chemical addiction but the brainwashing, and it was necessary first to explode the myths and delusions. Understand your enemy. Know his tactics, and you will easily defeat him.

I've spent most of my life trying to stop smoking and I've suffered weeks of black depression. When I finally stopped I went from a hundred a day to zero without one bad moment. It was enjoyable even during the withdrawal period, and I have never had the slightest pang since. On the contrary, it is the most wonderful thing that has happened in my life.

I couldn't understand why it had been so easy and it took me a long time to find out the reason. It was this. I knew for certain that I was never going to smoke again. During previous attempts, no matter how determined I was, I was basically *trying* to stop

94

smoking, hoping that if I could survive long enough without a cigarette, the urge would eventually go. Of course it didn't go because I was waiting for something to happen, and the more I moped about it, the more I wanted a cigarette, so the craving never went.

My final attempt was different. Like all smokers nowadays, I had been giving the problem serious thought. Up to then, whenever I failed, I had consoled myself with the thought that it would be easier next time. It had never occurred to me that I would have to go on smoking the rest of my life. This latter thought filled me with horror and started me thinking very deeply about the subject.

Instead of lighting up cigarettes subconsciously, I began to analyse my feelings as I was smoking them. This confirmed what I already knew. I wasn't enjoying them, and they were filthy and disgusting.

I started looking at non-smokers. Until then I had always regarded non-smokers as wishy-washy, unsociable, finicky people. However, when I examined them they appeared, if anything, stronger and more relaxed. They appeared to be able to cope with the stresses and strains of life, and they seemed to enjoy social functions more than the smokers. They certainly had more sparkle and zest than smokers.

I started talking to ex-smokers. Up to this point I had regarded ex-smokers as people who had been forced to give up smoking for health and money reasons and who were always secretly longing for a cigarette. A few did say, 'You get the odd pangs, but they are so few and far between they aren't worth bothering about.' But most said, 'Miss it? You must be joking. I have never felt better in my life.'

Talking to ex-smokers exploded another myth that I had always had in my mind. I had thought that there was an inherent weakness in me, and it suddenly dawned on me that all smokers go through this private nightmare. Basically I said to myself, 'Millions of people are stopping now and leading perfectly happy lives. I didn't need to do it before I started, and I can remember having to work hard to get used to the filthy things. So why do I need to do it now?' In any event I didn't enjoy smoking. I hated the whole filthy ritual and I didn't want to spend the rest of my life being the slave of this disgusting weed.

I then said to myself: 'Allen, WHETHER YOU LIKE IT OR NOT, YOU HAVE SMOKED YOUR LAST CIGARETTE.'

I knew, right from that point, that I would never smoke again. I wasn't expecting it to be easy; in fact, just the reverse. I fully believed that I was in for months of black depression and that I would spend the rest of my life having the occasional pang. Instead it has been absolute bliss right from the start.

It took me a long time to work out why it had been so easy and why this time I hadn't suffered those terrifying withdrawal pangs. The reason is that they do not exist. It is the doubt and uncertainty that causes the pangs. The beautiful truth is: IT IS EASY TO STOP SMOKING. It is only the indecision and moping about it that makes it difficult. Even while they are addicted to nicotine, smokers can go for relatively long periods at certain times in their lives without bothering about it. It is only when you want a cigarette but can't have one that you suffer.

Therefore the key to making it easy is to make stopping certain and final. Not to *hope* but to *know* you have kicked it, having made the decision. Never to doubt or question it. In fact, just the reverse – always to rejoice about it.

If you can be certain from the start, it will be easy. But how can you be certain from the start unless you know it is going to be easy? This is why the rest of the book is necessary. There are certain essential points and it is necessary to get them clear in your mind before you start.

1 Realize that you can achieve it. There is nothing different about you, and the only person who can make you smoke that next cigarette is you.

2 There is absolutely nothing to give up. On the contrary, there are enormous positive gains to be made. I do not only mean you will be healthier and richer. I mean you will enjoy the good times more and be less miserable during the bad times.

3 Get it clear in your head that there is no such thing as one cigarette. Smoking is a drug addiction and a chain reaction. By moaning about the odd cigarette you will only be punishing yourself needlessly.

4 See the whole business of smoking as not a sociable habit that might injure you but as drug addiction. Face up to the fact that, whether you like it or not, YOU HAVE GOT THE DISEASE. It will not go away because you put your head into the sand. Remember: like all crippling diseases, it not only lasts for life but gets worse and worse. The easiest time to cure it is *now*.

5 Separate the disease (i.e. the chemical addiction) from the frame of mind of being a smoker or a non-smoker. All smokers, if given the opportunity to go back to the time before they became hooked, would jump at that opportunity. You have that opportunity today! Don't even think about it as 'giving up' smoking. When you have made the final decision that you have smoked your last cigarette you will already be a non-smoker. A smoker is one of those poor wretches who have to go through life destroying themselves with cigarettes. A non-smoker is someone who doesn't. Once you have made that final decision, you have already achieved your object. Rejoice in the fact. Do not sit moping waiting for the chemical addiction to go. Get out and enjoy life immediately. Life is marvellous even when you are addicted to nicotine, and each day it will get better when you aren't.

The key to making it easy to give up smoking is to be certain that you will succeed in abstaining completely during the withdrawal period (maximum three weeks). If you are in the correct frame of mind, you will find it ridiculously easy.

By this stage, if you have opened your mind as I requested at the beginning, you will already have decided you are going to stop. You should now have a feeling of excitement, like a dog straining at the lead, unable to wait to get the poison out of your system.

If you have a feeling of doom and gloom, it will be for one of the following reasons.

1 Something has not gelled in your mind. Re-read the above five points, and ask yourself if you believe them to be true. If you doubt any point, re-read the appropriate sections in the book.
2 You fear failure itself. Do not worry. Just read on. You will succeed. The whole business of smoking is like a confidence trick on a gigantic scale. Intelligent people fall for confidence tricks, but it is only a fool who, having once found out about the trick, goes on kidding himself.
3 You agree with everything, but you are still miserable. Don't be! Open your eyes. Something marvellous is happening. You are about to escape from the prison.

It is essential to start with the correct frame of mind: isn't it marvellous that I am a non-smoker?

All we have to do now is to keep you in that frame of mind

during the withdrawal period, and the next few chapters deal with specific points to enable you to stay in that frame of mind during that time. After the withdrawal period you won't have to think that way. You will think that way automatically, and the only mystery in your life will be 'It is so obvious, why couldn't I see it before?' However, two important warnings:

1 Delay your plan to extinguish your last cigarette until you have finished the book.
2 I have mentioned several times a withdrawal period of up to three weeks. This can cause misunderstanding. First, you may subconsciously feel that you have to suffer for three weeks. You don't. Secondly, avoid the trap of thinking, 'Somehow I have just got to abstain for three weeks and then I will be free.' Nothing will actually happen after three weeks. You won't suddenly feel like an non-smoker. Non-smokers do not feel any different from smokers. If you are moping about stopping during the three weeks, in all probability you will still be moping about it after the three weeks. What I am saying is, if you can start right now by saying, 'I am never going to smoke again. Isn't it marvellous?' after three weeks all temptation will go. Whereas if you say, 'If only I can survive three weeks without a cigarette,' you will be dying for a cigarette after the three weeks are up (unintentional pun).

33

The Withdrawal Period

For up to three weeks after your last cigarette you may be subjected to withdrawal pangs. These consist of two quite separate factors.

1 The withdrawal pangs of nicotine, that empty, insecure feeling, like a hunger, which smokers identify as a craving or something to do with their hands.
2 The psychological trigger of certain events such as a telephone conversation.

It is the failure to understand and to differentiate between these two distinct factors that makes it so difficult for smokers to achieve success under the Willpower Method, and it's also the reason why many smokers who do achieve it fall into the trap again.

Although the withdrawal pangs of nicotine cause no physical pain, do not underestimate their power. We talk of 'hunger pains' if we go without food for a day; there may be 'tummy rumblings', but there is no physical pain. Even so, hunger is a powerful force, and we are likely to become very irritable when deprived of food. It is similar when our body is craving nicotine. The difference is that our body needs food but it doesn't need poison and with the right frame of mind the withdrawal pains are easily overcome and disappear very quickly.

If smokers can abstain for a few days under the Willpower Method, the craving for nicotine soon disappears. It is the second factor that causes the difficulty. The smoker has got into the habit of relieving his withdrawal pangs at certain times or occasions, which causes an association of ideas (e.g. 'I cannot enjoy a drink without a cigarette'). It may be easier to understand the effect with the help of an example.

You have a car for a few years, and let's say the indicator lever is on the left of the steering column. On your next car it is on the right (the law of sod). You know it is on the right, but for a couple of weeks you put the windscreen wipers on whenever you want to indicate.

Stopping smoking is similar. During the early days of the withdrawal period the trigger mechanism will operate at certain times. You will think, 'I want a cigarette.' It is essential to counter the brainwashing right from square one, then these automatic triggers will quickly disappear. Under the Willpower Method, because the smoker believes he is making a sacrifice, is moping about it and is waiting for the urge to smoke to go, far from removing these trigger mechanisms he is actually increasing them.

A common trigger is a meal, particularly one at a restaurant with friends. The ex-smoker is already miserable because he is being deprived of his cigarette. His friends light up and he feels even more deprived. Now he is not enjoying the meal or what should be a pleasant social occasion. Because of his association of the cigarette with the meal and the social occasion he is now suffering a triple blow, and the brainwashing is actually being increased. If he is resolute and can hold out long enough, he eventually accepts his lot and gets on with his life. However, part of the brainwashing remains, and I think the second most pathetic thing about smoking is the smoker who has given up for health or money reasons, yet even after several years still craves a cigarette on certain occasions. He is pining over an illusion that exists only in his mind and is needlessly torturing himself.

Even under my method responding to triggers is the most common failing. The ex-smoker tends to regard the cigarette as a sort of placebo or sugar pill. He thinks: 'I know the cigarette does nothing for me, but if I think it does, on certain occasions it will be a help to me.'

A sugar pill, although giving no actual physical help, can be a powerful psychological aid to relieve genuine symptoms and is therefore a benefit. The cigarette, however, is not a sugar pill. It creates the symptoms that it relieves and after a while ceases even to relieve these symptoms completely; the 'pill' is causing the disease, and quite apart from that it also happens to be the No. 1 killer poison in Western society.

You may find it easier to understand the effect when related to non-smokers or a smoker who has quit for several years. Take the

100

case of a wife who loses her husband. It is quite common at such times for a smoker, with the best intentions, to say, 'Have a cigarette. It will help calm you down.'

If the cigarette is accepted, it will not have a calming effect because the woman is not addicted to nicotine and there are no withdrawal pangs to relieve. At best all it will do is to give her a momentary psychological boost. As soon as the cigarette is extinguished, the original tragedy is still there. In fact, it will be increased because the woman is now suffering withdrawal pangs, and her choice is now either to endure them or to relieve them by smoking another cigarette and start the chain of misery. All the cigarette will have done is to give a momentary psychological boost. The same effect could have been achieved by offering a word of comfort or a drink. Many non-smokers and ex-smokers have become addicted to the weed as a result of such occasions.

It is essential to counter the brainwashing right from the start. Get it quite clear in your head: you don't need the cigarette, and you are only torturing yourself by continuing to regard it as some sort of prop or boost. There is no need to be miserable. Cigarettes do not make meals or social occasions; they ruin them. Remember too that the smokers at that meal are not smoking because they are enjoying the cigarette. They are smoking because they have got to. They are drug addicts. They cannot enjoy the meal or life without it.

Abandon the concept of the smoking habit as pleasurable in itself. Many smokers think, 'If only there were a clean cigarette.' There *are* clean cigarettes. Any smoker who tries herbal cigarettes soon finds out they are a waste of time. Get it clear in your mind that the only reason you have been smoking is to get the nicotine. Once you have got rid of the craving for nicotine you will have no more need to stick a cigarette in your mouth than in your ear.

Whether the pang is due to actual withdrawal symptoms (the empty feeling) or a trigger mechanism, accept it. The physical pain is non-existent, and with the right frame of mind cigarettes become no problem. Do not worry about withdrawal. The feeling itself isn't bad. It is the association with wanting a cigarette and then feeling denied that is the problem.

Instead of moping about it, say to yourself, 'I know what it is. It's the withdrawal pang from nicotine. That's what smokers suffer all their lives and that's what keeps them smoking. Non-smokers do not suffer these pangs. It is another of the many evils of this drug. Isn't it marvellous I am purging this evil from my body?'

In other words, for the next three weeks you will have a slight trauma inside your body, but during those weeks, and for the rest of your life, something marvellous will be happening. You will be ridding yourself of an awful disease. That bonus will more than outweigh the slight trauma, and you will actually enjoy the withdrawal pangs. They will become moments of pleasure.

Think of the whole business of stopping as an exciting game. Think of the nicotine monster as a sort of tape worm inside your stomach. You have got to starve him for three weeks, and he is going to try to trick you into lighting a cigarette to keep him alive.

At times he will try to make you miserable. At times you will be off guard. Someone may offer you a cigarette and you may forget that you have stopped. There is a slight feeling of deprivation when you remember. Be prepared for these traps in advance. Whatever the temptation, get it into your mind that it is only there because of the monster inside your body, and every time you resist the temptation you have dealt another mortal blow in the battle.

Whatever you do, don't try to forget about smoking. This is one of the things that causes smokers using the Willpower Method hours of depression. They try to get through each day hoping that eventually they'll just forget about it.

It is like not being able to sleep. The more you worry about it, the harder it becomes.

In any event you won't be able to forget about it. For the first few days the 'little monster' will keep reminding you, and you won't be able to avoid it; while there are still smokers and extensive cigarette promotions about, you will have constant reminders.

The point is, you have no need to forget. Nothing bad is happening. Something marvellous is taking place. Even if you are thinking about it a thousand times a day, SAVOUR EACH MOMENT. REMIND YOURSELF HOW MARVELLOUS IT IS TO BE FREE AGAIN. REMIND YOURSELF OF THE SHEER JOY OF NOT HAVING TO CHOKE YOURSELF ANY MORE.

As I have said, you will find that the pangs become moments of pleasure, and you will be surprised how quickly you will then forget about smoking.

Whatever you do – DO NOT DOUBT YOUR DECISION. Once you start to doubt, you will start to mope, and it will get worse.

Instead use the moment as a boost. If the cause is depression, remind yourself that's what cigarettes were doing to you. If you are offered one by a friend, take pride in saying, 'I'm happy to say I do not need them any more.' That will hurt him, but when he sees that it isn't bothering you he will be half way to joining you.

Remember that you had very powerful reasons for stopping in the first place. Remind yourself of the $x,000 that one cigarette will cost you, and ask yourself whether you really want to risk those fearful diseases. Above all, remember that the feeling is only temporary and each moment is a moment nearer to your goal.

Some smokers fear that they will have to spend the rest of their lives reversing the 'automatic triggers'. In other words, they believe that they will have to go through life kidding themselves that they don't really need a cigarette by the use of psychology. This is not so. Remember that the optimist sees the bottle as half full and the pessimist sees it as half empty. In the case of smoking, the bottle is empty and the smoker sees it as full. It is the smoker who has been brainwashed. Once you start telling yourself that you don't need to smoke, in a very short time you won't even need to say it because the beautiful truth is ... you do not need to smoke. It's the last thing you need to do; make sure it's not the last thing you do.

34

Just One Puff

This is the undoing of many smokers who try to stop under the Willpower Method. They will go through three or four days and then have the odd cigarette or a puff or two to tide them over. They do not realize the devastating effect this has on their morale.

For most smokers that first puff doesn't taste good, and this gives their conscious minds a boost. They think, 'Good. That wasn't enjoyable. I am losing the urge to smoke.' In fact, the reverse is the case. Get it clear in your mind – CIGARETTES NEVER WERE ENJOYABLE. Enjoyment wasn't the reason why you smoked. If smokers smoked for enjoyment, they'd never smoke more than one cigarette.

The only reason why you smoked was to feed that little monster. Just think: you had starved him for four days. How precious that one cigarette or just the puff must have been to him. You are not aware of it in your conscious mind, but the fix your body received will be communicated to your subconscious mind and all your sound preparation will be undermined. There will be a little voice at the back of your mind saying, 'In spite of all the logic, they are precious. I want another one.'

That little puff has two damaging effects.

1 It keeps the little monster alive in your body.
2 What's worse, it keeps the big monster alive in your mind. If you had the last puff, it will be easier to have the next one.

Remember: just one cigarette is how people get into smoking in the first place.

35

Will it be Harder for Me?

The combinations of factors that will determine how easily each individual smoker will give up are infinite. To start with, each of us has his own character, type of work, personal circumstances, timing, etc.

Certain professions may make it harder than others, but providing the brainwashing is removed it doesn't have to be so. A few individual examples will help.

It tends to be particularly difficult for members of the medical profession. We think it should be easier for doctors because they are more aware of the effects of ill-health and are seeing daily evidence of it. Although this supplies more forceful reasons for stopping, it doesn't make it any easier to do. The reasons are these.

1 The constant awareness of the health risks creates fear, which is one of the conditions under which we need to relieve our withdrawal pangs.
2 A doctor's work is exceedingly stressful, and he is usually not able to relieve the additional stress of withdrawal pangs while he is working.
3 He has the additional stress of guilt. He feels that he should be setting an example for the rest of the population. This puts more pressure on him and increases the feeling of deprivation.

During his hard-earned breaks, when the normal stress is momentarily relieved, that cigarette becomes very precious when he eventually relieves his withdrawal pangs. This is a form of casual smoking and applies to any situation where the smoker is forced to abstain for lengthy periods. Under the Willpower Method the smoker is miserable because he is being deprived. He is not enjoying the break or the cup of tea or coffee that goes with it. His sense of loss is therefore greatly increased, and, because of the association of ideas, the cigarette gets credit for the total situation. However, if you can first remove the brainwashing and stop moping about the cigarette, the break and the cup of tea can still be enjoyed even while the body is craving nicotine.

Another difficult situation is boredom, particularly when it is combined with periods of stress. Typical examples are drivers or housewives with young children. The work is stressful, yet much of the work is monotonous. During an attempt to stop under the Willpower Method the housewife has long periods in which to mope about her 'loss', which increases the feeling of depression.

Again this can be easily overcome if your frame of mind is correct. Do not worry that you are continually reminded that you have stopped smoking. Use such moments to rejoice in the fact that you are ridding yourself of the evil monster. If you have a positive frame of mind, these pangs can become moments of pleasure.

Remember, any smoker, regardless of age, sex, intelligence or profession, can find it easy and enjoyable to stop provided YOU FOLLOW ALL THE INSTRUCTIONS.

36

The Main Reasons for Failure

There are two main reasons for failure. The first is the influence of other smokers. At a weak moment or during a social occasion somebody will light up. I have already dealt with this topic at length. Use that moment to remind yourself that there is no such thing as one cigarette. Rejoice in the fact that you have broken the chain. Remember that the smoker envies you, and feel sorry for him. Believe me, he needs your pity.

The other main reason for failure is having a bad day. Get it clear in your mind before you start that, whether you are a smoker or a non-smoker, there are good days and bad days. Life is a matter of relativity, and you cannot have ups without having downs.

The problem with the Willpower Method of stopping is that as soon as the smoker has a bad day he starts moping for a cigarette, and all he does is make a bad day worse. The non-smoker is better equipped, not only physically but also mentally, to cope with the stresses and strains of life.

If you have a bad day during the withdrawal period, just take it on the chin. Remind yourself that you had bad days when you smoked (otherwise you wouldn't have decided to stop). Instead of moping about it, say to yourself something like, 'OK, today's not so good, but smoking is not going to cure it. Tomorrow will be better, and at least I have got a marvellous bonus at the moment. I have kicked that awful cigarette habit.'

When you are a smoker you have to block your mind to the bad side of smoking. Smokers never have smokers' coughs, just permanent colds. When your car breaks down in the middle of nowhere you light a cigarette, but are you happy and cheerful? Of course you aren't. Once you stop smoking the tendency is to blame everything that goes wrong in your life on the fact that you have stopped. Now if your car breaks down, you think, 'At times like this I would have lit a cigarette.' That's true, but what you forget is that the cigarette didn't solve the problem, and you are simply punishing yourself by moping for an illusory crutch. You are creating an impossible situation. You are miserable because you can't have the cigarette, and you'll be even more miserable if you do. You know that you have made the correct decision by stopping smoking, so don't punish yourself by ever doubting the decision.

Remember: a positive mental approach is essential – always.

37

Substitutes

Substitutes include chewing gum, sweets, peppermints, herbal cigarettes, pills. DO NOT USE ANY OF THEM. They make it harder, not easier. If you do get a pang and use a substitute, it will prolong the pang and make it harder. What you are really saying is 'I need to smoke or fill the void.' It will be like giving in to a hijacker or the tantrums of a child. It will just keep the pangs coming and prolong the torture. In any event the substitutes will not relieve the pangs. Your craving is for nicotine, not food. All it will do is keep you thinking about smoking. Remember these points:

1 There is no substitute for nicotine.
2 You do not need nicotine. It is not food; it is poison. When the pangs come remind yourself that it is smokers who suffer withdrawal pangs, not non-smokers. See them as another evil of the drug. See them as the death of a monster.
3 Remember: cigarettes create the void; they do not fill it. The quicker you teach your brain that you do not need to smoke, or do anything else in its place, the sooner you will be free.

In particular, avoid chewing gum or any other product that contains nicotine. The theory is that you stop smoking and that while you break the habit you keep nicotine in your body and therefore do not suffer bad withdrawal pangs. In practice it actually makes it harder to stop, for this reason. In the case of cigarettes the habit is feeding withdrawal symptoms. Nicotine gives you no benefit. You smoke only to relieve the withdrawal pangs, and the habit dies with the pangs. The withdrawal pangs are so slight that there is no need to relieve them. The main problem in smoking, as I have already explained, is not the physical addiction but the *mental* brainwashing. All that nicotine chewing gum does is to prolong the chemical addiction, which in turn prolongs the mental addiction.

There are many ex-smokers who are now hooked on nicotine chewing gum. There are also many people hooked on the gum who are still smoking.

Do not kid yourself by thinking the gum tastes awful. Just remember – so did that first cigarette.

All substitutes have exactly the same effect as nicotine chewing gum. I'm now talking about this business of 'I can't have a cigarette, so I'll have ordinary chewing gum, or sweets, or peppermints to help fill the void.' Although the empty feeling of wanting a cigarette is indistinguishable from hunger for food, one will not satisfy the other. In fact, if anything is designed to make you want a cigarette, it's stuffing yourself with chewing gum or peppermints.

But the chief evil of substitutes is that they prolong the real problem, which is the brainwashing. Do you need a substitute for 'flu when it's over? Of course you don't. By saying 'I need a substitute for smoking' what you are really saying is 'I am making a sacrifice.' The depression associated with the Willpower Method is caused by the fact that the smoker believes he is making a sacrifice. All you will be doing is to substitute one problem for another. There is no pleasure in stuffing yourself with sweets. You will just get fat and miserable, and in no time at all you'll be back on the weed.

Remember, you don't need a substitute. Those pangs are a craving for poison and will soon be gone. Let that be your prop for the next few days. *Enjoy* ridding your body of poison and your mind of slavery and dependence.

If, because your appetite is better, you eat more at main meals and put on a couple of pounds during the next few days, don't worry about it. When you experience the 'moment of revelation' that I describe later you will have confidence, and you'll find that any problem you have that is capable of being solved by positive thinking you will be able to solve, including eating habits. But what you mustn't do is to start picking between meals. If you do, you will get fat and miserable and you will never know when you've kicked the weed. You'll just be moving the problem instead of getting rid of it.

38

Should I Avoid
Temptation Situations?

I have been categorical in my advice so far and would ask you to treat this advice as instruction rather than suggestion. I am categorical, first, because there are sound, practical reasons for my advice and, second, because those reasons have been backed up by thousands of case studies.

On the question of whether or not to try to avoid temptation situations during the withdrawal period, I regret that I cannot be categorical. Each smoker will need to decide for himself. I can, however, make what I hope will be helpful suggestions.

I repeat that it is fear that keeps us smoking all our lives, and this fear consists of two distinct phases.

1   How can I survive without a cigarette?
    This fear is the panic feeling that smokers get when they are out late at night and their cigarettes begin to run out. The fear isn't caused by withdrawal pangs but is the psychological fear of dependency – you cannot survive without a cigarette. It actually reaches its height when you are smoking your last cigarette; at that time your withdrawal pangs are at their lowest.

    It is the fear of the unknown, the sort of fear that people have when they are learning to dive. The diving board is 1 foot high but seems to be 6 feet high. The water is 6 feet deep but appears to be 1 foot deep. It takes courage to launch yourself. You are convinced you are going to smash your head. The launching is the hardest part. If you can find the courage to do it, the rest is easy.

    This explains why many otherwise strong-willed smokers either have never attempted to stop or can survive only a few hours when they do. In fact, there are some smokers on about twenty a day who, when they decide to stop, actually smoke

111

their next cigarette more quickly than if they had not decided to stop. The decision causes panic, which is stressful. This is one of the occasions when the brain triggers the instruction 'Have a cigarette', but now you can't have one. You are being deprived – more stress. The trigger starts again – quickly the fuse blows and you light up.

Don't worry. That panic is just psychological. It is the fear that you are dependent. The beautiful truth is that you are not even when you are still addicted to nicotine. Do not panic. Just trust me and launch yourself.

2 The second phase of fear is longer-term. It involves the fear that certain situations in the future will not be enjoyable without a cigarette or that the ex-smoker will not be able to cope with a trauma without the cigarette. Don't worry. If you can launch yourself you will find the opposite to be the case.

The avoidance of temptation itself falls into two main categories.

1 'I will keep my cigarettes available, although I will not smoke them. I will feel more confident knowing they are there.'

I find the failure rate with people who do this is far higher than with people who discard them. I believe this is due mainly to the fact that if you have a bad moment during the withdrawal period, it is easy to light up a readily available cigarette. If you have the indignity of having to go out and buy a packet you are more likely to overcome the temptation, and in any event the pang will probably have passed before you get to the tobacconist's.

However, I believe the main reason for the higher failure rate in these cases is that the smoker does not feel completely committed to stopping in the first place. Remember the two essentials to succeed are:

Certainty.
'Isn't it marvellous that I do not need to smoke any more?'

In either case, why on earth do you need cigarettes? If you still feel the need to keep cigarettes on your person, I would suggest that you re-read the book first. It means that something hasn't gelled.

2 'Should I avoid stressful or social occasions during the withdrawal period?'

My advice is, yes, try to avoid stressful situations. There is no sense in putting undue pressure on yourself.

In the case of social events my advice is the reverse. No, go out and enjoy yourself straight away. You do not need cigarettes even while you are still addicted to nicotine. Go to a party, and rejoice in the fact that you do not have to smoke. It will quickly prove to you the beautiful truth that life is so much better without cigarettes – and just think how much better it will be when the little monster has left your body, together with all that poison.

39

The Moment of Revelation

The moment of revelation usually takes place about three weeks after a smoker stops. The sky appears to become brighter, and it is the moment when the brainwashing ends completely, when, instead of telling yourself you do not need to smoke, you suddenly realize that the last thread is broken and you can enjoy the rest of your life without ever needing to smoke again. It is also usually from this point that you start looking at other smokers as objects of pity.

Smokers using the Willpower Method do not normally experience this moment because, although they are glad to be ex-smokers, they go through life believing they are making a sacrifice.

The more you smoked, the more marvellous this moment is, and it lasts a lifetime.

I consider I have been very fortunate in this life and had some wonderful moments, but the most wonderful of all was that moment of revelation. With all the other highlights of my life, although I can remember they were happy times, I can never recapture the actual feeling. I can never get over the joy of not having to smoke any more. If ever I am feeling low and need a boost nowadays, I just think how lovely it is not to be hooked on that awful weed. Half the people who contact me after they have kicked the weed say exactly the same thing, that it was the most marvellous event of their lives. Ah! What pleasure you have to come!

With an additional five years' feedback, both from the book and from my consultations, I have learned that in most cases the moment of revelation occurs not after three weeks, as stated above, but within a few days.

In my own case it happened before I'd extinguished my last cigarette, and on many occasions in my early consultancy sessions, during the one-to-one period, before I'd even got to the end of a session smokers would say something like: 'You needn't say

114

another word, Allen. I can see it all so clearly, I know I'll never smoke again.' In the group sessions I've learned to tell when it happens without individual smokers saying anything. From the letters I receive I'm also aware that it frequently happens with the book.

Ideally if you follow all the instructions and understand the psychology completely, it should happen to you immediately.

Nowadays at my consultations I say to smokers that it takes about five days for the noticeable physical withdrawal to go and about three weeks for an ex-smoker to get completely free. In one way I dislike giving such guidelines. It can cause two problems. The first is that I put in people's minds the suggestion that they will have to suffer for between five days and three weeks. The second is that the ex-smoker tends to think, 'If I can survive for five days or three weeks, I can expect a real boost at the end of that period.' However, he may have five pleasant days or three pleasant weeks, followed by one of those disastrous days that strike both non-smokers and smokers, which have nothing to do with smoking but are caused by other factors in our lives. There our ex-smoker is, waiting for the moment of revelation, and what he experiences is depression instead. It could destroy his confidence.

If I don't give any guidelines, however, the ex-smoker can spend the rest of his life waiting for nothing to happen. I suspect that this is what happens to the vast majority of smokers who stop with the help of Willpower Method.

At one time I was tempted to say that revelation should happen immediately. But if I did that and it didn't happen immediately, the ex-smoker would lose confidence and would think it was never going to happen.

People often ask me about the significance of the five days and three weeks. Are they just periods that I've drawn out of the blue? No. They are obviously not definite dates, but they reflect an accumulation of feedback over the years. About five days after stopping is when the ex-smoker ceases to have smoking as the main occupation of his mind. Most ex-smokers experience the moment of revelation around this period. What usually happens is you are in one of those stressful or social situations that once you couldn't cope with or enjoy without a cigarette. You suddenly realize that not only are you enjoying or coping with it but the thought of having a cigarette has never even occurred to you. From that point on it is usually plain sailing. That's when you know you can be free.

I have noticed from my previous attempts using the Willpower Method, and from feedback from other smokers, that around the three-week period is when most serious attempts to stop smoking fail. I believe that what usually happens is that after about three weeks you sense that you have lost the desire to smoke. You need to prove this to yourself, and you light a cigarette. It tastes weird. You've proved you have kicked it. But you've also put fresh nicotine into your body, and nicotine is what your body has been craving for three weeks. As soon as you extinguish that cigarette, the nicotine starts to leave your body. Now a little voice is saying, 'You haven't kicked it. You want another one.' You don't light another one straight away because you don't want to get hooked again. You allow a safe period to pass. When you are next tempted you are able to say to yourself, 'But I didn't get hooked again, so there's no harm in having another.' You are already on your way down the slippery slope.

The key to the problem is not to wait for the moment of revelation but to realize that once you extinguish that last cigarette it is finished. You've already done all you need to do. You've cut off the supply of nicotine. No force on earth can prevent you from being free unless you mope about it or wait for revelation. Go and enjoy life; cope with it right from the start. That way you'll soon experience the moment.

40

That Last Cigarette

Having decided on your timing, you are now ready to smoke that last cigarette. Before you do so, check on the two essentials:

1 Do you feel certain of success?
2 Have you a feeling of doom and gloom or a sense of excitement that you are about to achieve something marvellous?

If you have any doubts, re-read the book first.

When you feel quite ready, smoke your last cigarette. Do it alone, and smoke it consciously. Concentrate on every puff. Concentrate on the taste and smell. Concentrate on the cancerous fumes going into your lungs. Concentrate on the poisons silting up your arteries and veins. Concentrate on the nicotine going into your body.

When you put it out, just think how marvellous it will be not to have to go on doing it. The joy of being freed from slavery is like coming out of a world of black shadows into a world of sunshine.

41

A Final Warning

No smoker, given the chance of going back to the time before he became hooked with the knowledge he has now, would opt to start. Many of the smokers who consult me are convinced that if I could only help them stop, they would never dream of smoking again, and yet thousands of smokers successfully kick the habit for many years and lead perfectly happy lives, only to get trapped once again.

I trust that this book will help you to find it relatively easy to stop smoking. But be warned: smokers who find it easy to stop find it easy to start again.

DO NOT FALL FOR THIS TRAP.

No matter how long you have stopped or how confident you are that you will never become hooked again, make it a rule of life not to smoke for any reason. Resist the millions of pounds that the tobacco companies spend on promotion, and remember they are pushing the No. 1 killer drug and poison. You wouldn't be tempted to try heroin, and cigarettes kill hundreds of thousands more people in Western society than heroin does.

Remember, that first cigarette will do nothing for you. You will have no withdrawal pangs to relieve, and it will taste awful. What it will do is to put nicotine into your body, and a little voice at the back of your mind will be saying, 'You want another one.' Then you have got the choice of being miserable for a while or starting the whole filthy chain again.

42

Five Years' Feedback

Since the original publication of this book I now have five years' feedback, both from my own consultations and from the book itself. Originally it was a struggle. My method was pooh-poohed by the so-called experts. Now smokers fly in from all over the world to attend my consultations, and more members of the medical profession attend them than members of any other profession. The book is already regarded in the UK as the most effective aid for stopping smoking, and its reputation is rapidly spreading to the rest of the world.

I'm not a do-gooder. My war – which, I emphasize, is not against smokers but against smoking – I wage for the purely selfish reason that I enjoy it. Every time I hear of a smoker escaping from the prison I get a feeling of great pleasure, even when it has nothing to do with me. You can imagine also the immense pleasure I obtain from the thousands of grateful letters that I have received over the years.

There has also been considerable frustration. The frustration is caused mainly by two main categories of smoker. First, in spite of the warning in the previous chapter, I am disturbed by the number of smokers who find it easy to stop, yet get hooked again and find they can't succeed the next time. This applies not only to readers of the book but also to my consultations.

A man telephoned me about two years ago. He was very distraught; in fact, he was crying. He said, 'I'll pay you £1,000 if you can help me stop for a week. I know if I can just survive a week, I'll be able to do it.' I told him that I charge a fixed fee and that was all he need pay. He attended a group session and, much to his surprise, found it easy to stop. He sent me a very nice thank-you letter.

Practically the last thing I say to ex-smokers leaving my sessions is: 'Remember, you must never smoke another cigarette.' This particular man said, 'Have no fear, Allen. If I manage to stop, I'll definitely never smoke again.'

I could tell that the warning hadn't really registered. I said, 'I know you feel like that at the moment, but how will you feel six months on?'

He said, 'Allen, I will never smoke again.'

About a year later there was another phone call. 'Allen, I had a small cigar at Christmas, and now I'm back on forty cigarettes a day.'

I said, 'Do you remember when you first phoned? You hated it so much you were going to pay me £1,000 if you could stop for a week.'

'I remember. Haven't I been stupid?'

'Do you remember you promised me you would never smoke again?'

'I know. I'm a fool.'

It's like finding someone up to his neck in a bog and about to go under. You help pull him out. He is grateful to you and then, six months later, dives straight back into the bog.

Ironically, when this man attended a subsequent session he said, 'Can you believe it? I offered to pay my son £1,000 if he hadn't smoked by his twenty-first birthday. I paid up. He's now twenty-two and puffing away like a chimney. I can't believe he could be so stupid.'

I said, 'I don't see how you can call him stupid. At least he avoided the trap for twenty-two years, and he doesn't know the misery he's in for. You knew it as well as anyone and survived only a year.'

Smokers who find it easy to stop and start again pose a special problem, and I will shortly be publishing another book to help them. In the meantime when you get free PLEASE, PLEASE, DON'T MAKE THE SAME MISTAKE. Smokers believe that such people start again because they are still hooked and are missing the cigarette. In fact, they find stopping so easy that they lose their fear of smoking. They think, 'I can have an odd cigarette. Even if I do get hooked again, I'll find it easy to stop.'

I'm afraid it just doesn't work that way. It's easy to stop smoking, but it's impossible to try to control the addiction. The one thing that is essential to becoming a non-smoker is *not to smoke*.

The other category of ex-smokers that causes me frustration is those who are just too frightened to make the attempt or, when they do, find it a great struggle. The main difficulties appear to be the following.

1 Fear of failure. There is no disgrace in failure, but not to try is plain stupidity. Look at it this way – you're on a hiding to nothing. The worst thing that can happen is that you fail, in which case you are no worse off than you are now. Just think how wonderful it would be to succeed. If you don't make the attempt, you have already guaranteed failure.

2 Fear of panic and of being miserable. Don't worry about it. Just think: what awful thing could happen to you if you never smoked another cigarette? Absolutely none. Terrible things will happen if you do. In any case, the panic is caused by cigarettes and will soon be gone. The greatest gain is to be rid of that fear. Do you really believe that smokers are prepared to have their arms and legs removed for the pleasure they get from smoking? If you find yourself feeling panicky, deep breathing will help. If you are with other people and they are getting you down, go away from them. Escape to the garage or an empty office or wherever.

If you feel like crying, don't be ashamed. Crying is nature's way of relieving tension. No one has ever had a good cry without feeling better afterwards. One of the awful things we do to young boys is to teach them not to cry. You see them trying to fight the tears back, but watch the jaw grinding away. As Britons, we teach ourselves to keep the upper lip stiff, not to show any emotions. We are meant to show emotions, not to try to bottle them up inside us. Scream or shout or have a tantrum. Kick a cardboard box or filing cabinet. Regard your struggle as a boxing match that you cannot lose.

No one can stop time. Every moment that passes that little monster inside you is dying. Enjoy your inevitable victory.

3 Not following the instructions. Incredibly, some smokers say to me, 'Your method just didn't work for me.' They then describe how they ignored not only one instruction but practically all of them. (For clarification I will summarize these in the check list at the end of the chapter.)

4 Misunderstanding instructions. The chief problems appear to be these.

(a) 'I can't stop thinking about smoking.' Of course you can't, and if you try, you will create a phobia and be miserable. It's like trying to get to sleep at night; the more you try, the harder it becomes. I think about smoking 90 per cent of my waking and sleeping life. It's what you are thinking that's

121

important. If you are thinking, 'Oh, I'd love a cigarette,' or 'When will I be free?' you'll be miserable. If you are thinking, 'YIPPEE! I am free!' you'll be happy.

(b) 'When will the physical craving go?' The nicotine leaves your body very rapidly. But it is impossible to tell when *your* body will stop craving nicotine. That empty, insecure feeling is caused by normal hunger, depression or stress. All the cigarette does is to increase the level of it. This is why smokers who stop by using the Willpower Method are never quite sure when they've kicked it. Even after the body has stopped craving nicotine and they are suffering normal hunger or stress, their brain is still saying, 'That means you want a cigarette.' The point is you don't have to wait for the nicotine craving to go; it is so slight that we don't even know it's there. We know it only as feeling 'I want a cigarette.' When you leave the dentist after the final session, do you wait for your jaw to stop aching? Of course you don't. You get on with your life. Even though your jaw's still aching, you are elated.

(c) Waiting for the moment of revelation. If you wait for it, you are just causing another phobia. I once stopped for three weeks under the Willpower Method. I met an old school friend and ex-smoker. He said, 'How are you getting on?'

I said, 'I've survived three weeks.'

He said, 'What do you mean, you've survived three weeks?'

I said, 'I've gone three weeks without a cigarette.'

He said, 'What are you going to do? *Survive* the rest of your life? What are you waiting for? You've done it. You're a non-smoker.'

I thought, 'He's absolutely right. What am I waiting for?' Unfortunately, because I didn't fully understand the nature of the trap at that time, I was soon back in it, but the point was noted. You become a non-smoker when you extinguish your last cigarette. The important thing is to be a happy non-smoker from the start.

(d) 'I am still craving cigarettes.' Then you are being very stupid. How can you claim, 'I want to be a non-smoker,' and then say, 'I want a cigarette'? That's a contradiction. If you say, 'I want a cigarette,' you are saying, 'I want to be a smoker.' Non-smokers don't want to smoke cigarettes. You already know what you really want to be, so stop punishing yourself.

(e) 'I've opted out of life.' Why? All you have to do is stop choking yourself. You don't have to stop living. Look, it's as simple as this. For the next few days you'll have a slight trauma in your life. Your body will physically crave nicotine. Now, bear this in mind: you are no worse off than you were. This is what you have been suffering the whole of your smoking life, every time you have been asleep or in a church, supermarket or library. It didn't seem to bother you when you were a smoker, and if you don't stop, you'll go on suffering this distress for the rest of your life. Cigarettes don't make meals or drinks or social occasions; they ruin them. Even while your body is still craving nicotine, meals and social occasions are marvellous. Life is marvellous. Go to social functions, even if there are twenty smokers there. Remember that *you* are not being deprived; *they* are. Every one of them would love to be in your position. Enjoy being the prima donna and the centre of attention. Stopping smoking is a wonderful conversation point, particularly when smokers see that you are happy and cheerful. They'll think that you are incredible. The important point is that you'll be enjoying life right from the start. There's no need to envy them. They'll be envying you.

(f) 'I am miserable and irritable.' That is because you haven't followed my instructions. Find out which one it is. Some people understand and believe everything I say but still start off with a feeling of doom and gloom, as if something terrible were happening. You are doing not only what you'd like to do but what every smoker on the planet would like to do. With any method of stopping, what the ex-smoker is trying to achieve is a certain frame of mind, so that whenever he thinks about smoking he says to himself, 'YIPPEE! I'M FREE!' If that's your object, why wait? Start off in that frame of mind and never lose it. The rest of the book is designed to make you understand why there is no alternative.

THE CHECK LIST

If you follow these simple instructions, you cannot fail.

1 Make a solemn vow that you will never, ever, smoke, chew or suck anything that contains nicotine, and stick to your vow.
2 Get this clear in your mind: there is absolutely nothing to *give*

up. By that I don't mean simply that you will be better off as a non-smoker (you've known that all your life); neither do I mean that although there is no rational reason why you smoke, you must get some form of pleasure or crutch from it or you wouldn't do it. What I mean is, there is no genuine pleasure or crutch in smoking. It is just an illusion, like banging your head against a wall to make it pleasant when you stop.

3 There is no such thing as a confirmed smoker. You are just one of the millions who have fallen for this subtle trap. Like millions of other ex-smokers who once thought they couldn't escape, you have escaped.

4 If at any time in your life you were to weigh up the pros and cons of smoking, the conclusion would always be, a dozen times over, 'Stop doing it. You are a fool.' Nothing will ever change that. It always has been that way, and it always will be. Having made what you know to be the correct decision, don't ever torture yourself doubting it.

5 Don't try *not* to think about smoking or worry that you are thinking about it constantly. But whenever you do think about it – whether it be today, tomorrow or the rest of your life – think, 'YIPPEE! I'M A NON-SMOKER!'

6 DO NOT use any form of substitute.
DO NOT keep your own cigarettes.
DO NOT avoid other smokers.
DO NOT change your lifestyle in any way purely because you've stopped smoking.

If you follow the above instructions, you will soon experience the moment of revelation. But:

7 Don't wait for that moment to come. Just get on with your life. Enjoy the highs and cope with the lows. You will find that in no time at all the moment will arrive.

43

Help the Smoker Left on the Sinking Ship

Smokers are panicking nowadays. They sense that there is a change in society. Smoking is now regarded as an unsociable habit, even by smokers themselves. They also sense that the whole thing is coming to an end. Millions of smokers are now stopping, and all smokers are conscious of this fact.

Every time a smoker leaves the sinking ship, the ones left on it feel more miserable. Every smoker instinctively knows that it is ridiculous to pay good money for dried leaves rolled up in paper, to set light to them and to breathe cancer-triggering tar into his lungs. If you still don't think it is silly, try sticking a burning cigarette in your ear and ask yourself what the difference is. Just one. You cannot get the nicotine that way. If you can stop sticking cigarettes in your mouth, you won't need the nicotine.

Smokers cannot find a rational reason for smoking, but if someone else is doing it, they do not feel quite so silly.

Smokers blatantly lie about their habit, not only to others but to themselves. They have to. The brainwashing is essential if they are to retain some self-respect. They feel the need to justify their habit, not only to themselves but to non-smokers. They are therefore for ever advertising the illusory advantages of smoking.

If a smoker stops by the Willpower Method, he still feels deprived and tends to become a moaner. All this does is to confirm to other smokers how right they are to keep smoking.

If the ex-smoker succeeds in kicking the habit, he is grateful that he no longer has to go through life choking himself or wasting money. But he is not doing it and has no need to justify himself, he doesn't sit there saying how marvellous it is not to be smoking. He will do that only if he is asked, and smokers won't ask that question. They wouldn't like the answer. Remember, it is fear that keeps them smoking, and they would rather keep their heads in the sand.

The only time they ask that question is when it is time to stop.

Help the smoker. Remove these fears. Tell him how marvellous it is not to have to go through life choking yourself, how lovely it is to wake up in the morning feeling fit and healthy instead of wheezing and coughing, how wonderful it is to be free of slavery, to be able to enjoy the whole of your life, to be rid of those awful black shadows.

Or, better still, get him to read the book.

It is essential not to belittle the smoker by indicating that he is polluting the atmosphere or is in some way unclean. There is a common conception that the ex-smoker is the worst in this respect. I believe this conception has some substance, and I think this is due to the Willpower Method of stopping. Because the ex-smoker, although he has kicked the habit, retains part of the brainwashing, part of him still believes that he has made a sacrifice. He feels vulnerable, and his natural defensive mechanism is to attack the smoker. This may help the ex-smoker, but it does nothing to help the smoker. All it does is put his back up, make him feel even more wretched and consequently make his need for a cigarette even greater.

Although the change in society's attitude to smoking is the main reason why millions of smokers are kicking the habit, it doesn't make it easier for them to do so. In fact, it makes it a great deal harder. Most smokers nowadays believe they are stopping mainly for health reasons. This is not strictly true. Although the enormous health risk is obviously the chief reason for quitting the habit, smokers have been killing themselves for years and it made not the slightest difference. The main reason why smokers are stopping is because society is beginning to see the habit for what it actually is: filthy drug addiction. The enjoyment was always an illusion; this attitude removes this illusion, so that the smoker is left with nothing.

The complete ban on smoking in London's Underground system is a classic example of the smoker's dilemma. The smoker either takes the attitude: 'OK, if I cannot smoke on the train, I will find another means of travel,' which does no good but merely loses London Transport valuable revenue, or he says: 'Fine, it will help me cut down on my smoking.' The result of this is that instead of smoking one or two cigarettes on the train, neither of which he would have enjoyed, he abstains for an hour. During this enforced period of abstinence, however, not only will he be mentally deprived and waiting for his reward but his body will have been craving nicotine – and, oh, how precious that cigarette will be when he is eventually allowed to light up.

Enforced abstinences do not actually cut down the intake because the smoker just indulges himself in more cigarettes when he is eventually allowed to smoke. All it does is to ingrain in the smoker's mind how precious cigarettes are and how dependent he is upon them.

I think the most insidious aspect of this enforced abstinence is its effect on pregnant women. We allow unfortunate teenagers to be bombarded with massive advertising that gets them hooked in the first place. Then, at what is probably the most stressful period in their lives, when in their deluded minds they need cigarettes most of all, the medical profession blackmails them into giving up because of the harm they are causing the baby. Many are unable to do so and are forced, through no fault of their own, to suffer a guilt complex for the rest of their lives. Many of them succeed and are pleased to do so, thinking, 'Fine, I will do this for the baby and after nine months I will be cured anyway.' Then comes the pain and fear of labour, followed by the biggest 'high' of their lives. The pain and fear are over, and the beautiful, new baby has arrived – and the old trigger mechanism comes into operation. Part of the brainwashing is still there, and almost before the cord has been cut, the girl has a cigarette in her mouth. The elation of the occasion blocks the foul taste from her mind. She has no intention of becoming hooked again. 'Just the one cigarette.' Too late! She is already hooked. Nicotine has got into her body again. The old craving will start, and even if she doesn't become hooked again straight away, post-natal depression will probably catch her out.

It is strange that although heroin addicts are criminals in law, our society's attitude is quite rightly 'What can we do to help the pathetic individuals?' Let us adopt the same attitude to the poor smoker. He is not smoking because he wants to but because he thinks he has got to, and, unlike the heroin addict, he usually has to suffer years and years of mental and physical torture. We always say a quick death is better than a slow one, so do not envy the poor smoker. He needs your pity.

44

Advice to Non-smokers

HELP GET YOUR SMOKING FRIENDS OR RELATIVES TO READ THIS BOOK

First study the contents of this book and try to put yourself in the place of the smoker.

Do not force him to read this book or try to stop him smoking by telling him he is ruining his health or wasting his money. He already knows this better than you do. Smokers do not smoke because they enjoy it or because they want to. They only tell themselves and other people this in order to retain self-respect. They smoke because they feel dependent on cigarettes, because they think that the cigarette relaxes them and gives them courage and confidence and that life will never be enjoyable without a cigarette. If you try to force a smoker to stop, he feels like a trapped animal and wants his cigarette even more. This may turn him into a secret smoker and in his mind the cigarette will become even more precious (see chapter 26).

Instead, concentrate on the other side of the coin. Get him into the company of other heavy smokers who have kicked the habit (there are 10 million of them in Britain alone). Get them to tell the smoker how they too thought they were hooked for life and how much better life is as a non-smoker.

Once you have got him believing that he can stop, his mind will start opening. Then start explaining the delusion created by withdrawal pangs. Not only are the cigarettes not giving him a boost but it is they that are destroying his confidence and making him irritable and unrelaxed.

He should now be ready to read this book himself. He will be expecting to read pages and pages about lung cancer, heart diseases, etc. Explain that the approach is completely different and that references to illness are just a small fraction of the material in the book.

HELP DURING THE WITHDRAWAL PERIOD

Whether the ex-smoker is suffering or not, assume that he is. Do not try to minimize his suffering by telling him it is easy to stop; he can do that himself. Instead keep telling him how proud you are, how much better he is looking, how much sweeter he smells, how much easier his breathing is. It is particularly important to keep doing this. When a smoker makes an attempt to stop, the euphoria of the attempt and the attention he gets from friends and colleagues can help him along. However, they tend to forget quickly, so keep that praise going.

Because he is not talking about smoking, you may think he has forgotten about it and don't want to remind him. Usually the complete opposite is the case with the Willpower Method, as the ex-smoker tends to be obsessed by nothing else. So do not be frightened to bring the subject up, and keep praising him; he will tell you if he doesn't want you to remind him of smoking.

Go out of your way to relieve him of pressures during the withdrawal period. Try to think of ways of making his life interesting and enjoyable.

This can also be a trying period for non-smokers. If one member of a group is irritable, it can cause general misery all round. So anticipate this if the ex-smoker is feeling irritable. He may well take it out on you, but do not retaliate; it is at this time that he needs your praise and sympathy the most. If you are feeling irritable yourself, try not to show it.

One of the tricks I used to play when trying to give up with the aid of the Willpower Method was to get into a tantrum, hoping that my wife or friends would say, 'I cannot bear to see you suffering like this. For goodness sake, have a cigarette.' The smoker then does not lose face, as he isn't 'giving in' – he has been instructed. If the ex-smoker uses this ploy, on no account encourage him to smoke. Instead say, 'If that is what cigarettes do to you, thank goodness you will soon be free. How marvellous that you had the courage and sense to give up.'

Finale: Help End This Scandal

In my opinion, cigarette smoking is the biggest scandal in Western society, including nuclear weapons.

Surely the very basis of civilization, the reason why the human species has advanced so far, is that we are capable of communicating our knowledge and experiences not only to each other but to future generations. Even the lower species find it necessary to warn their offspring of the pitfalls in life.

If nuclear weapons do not go off, there is no problem. The people who advocate nuclear armament can carry on saying smugly, 'They are keeping the peace.' If they do go off, they will solve the smoking problem and every other problem, and a bonus for the politicians is that there will be nobody around to say, 'You were wrong' (I wonder if this is why they support nuclear weapons).

However, much as I disagree with nuclear weapons, at least such decisions are made in good faith, in the genuine belief that they help mankind, whereas with smoking, the true facts are known. Maybe during the last war people genuinely believed that cigarettes gave you courage and confidence. Today the authorities know that is a fallacy. Just watch the cigarette adverts nowadays. They make no claims about relaxation or pleasure. The only claims they make are about size or the quality of the tobacco. Why should we be worried about the size and quality of a poison?

The sheer hypocrisy is incredible. As a society we get uptight about glue sniffing and heroin addiction. Compared with cigarette smoking, these problems are mere pimples in our society. Sixty per cent of the population have been addicted to nicotine, and most of them spend the bulk of their pocket money on cigarettes. Tens of thousands of people have their lives ruined every year because they become hooked. Smoking is by far the biggest killer in Western society and yet the biggest vested interest is our own

130

government. It makes billions every year out of the misery of nicotine addicts, and the tobacco empires are allowed to spend hundreds of millions per year advertising the filth.

How clever that cigarette companies print that health warning on packets, and our government spends a pittance on TV campaigns involving cancer scares, bad breath and legs being chopped off, and then they justify themselves morally by saying, 'We have warned you of the danger. It is your choice.' The smoker doesn't have the choice any more than the heroin addict does. Smokers do not decide to become hooked; they are lured into a subtle trap. If smokers had the choice, the only smokers tomorrow morning would be the youngsters starting out believing they could stop any time they wanted to.

Why the phoney standards? Why are heroin addicts seen as criminals, yet can register as addicts and get free heroin and proper medical treatment to help get off it? Just try registering as a nicotine addict. You cannot get cigarettes at cost. You have to pay three times the true value and every Budget Day you will be screwed further by the government. As if the smoker hadn't got troubles enough!

If you go to your doctor for help, either he will tell you, 'Stop doing it, it's killing you,' which you already know, or he will prescribe a chewing gum that will cost you a prescription fee and actually contains the drug you are trying to kick.

Scare campaigns do not help smokers to stop. They make it harder. All they do is to frighten smokers, which makes them want to smoke even more. It doesn't even prevent teenagers from becoming hooked. Teenagers know that cigarettes kill, but they also know one cigarette will not do it. Because the habit is so prevalent, sooner or later the teenager, through social pressures or curiosity, will try just one cigarette. And *because* it tastes so awful, he will probably become hooked.

Why do we allow this scandal to go on? Why doesn't our government come out with a proper campaign? Why doesn't it tell us that nicotine is a drug and a killer poison, that it does not relax you or give you confidence but destroys your nerves and that it can take just one cigarette to become hooked?

I remember reading H. G. Wells's *The Time Machine*. The book describes an incident in the distant future in which a man falls into a river. His companions merely sit around the bank like cattle, oblivious to his cries of desperation. I found that incident inhuman and very disturbing. I find the general apathy of our society to the smoking problem very similar. We allow darts tournaments sponsored by tobacco companies to be televised during peak viewing hours. There is a cry of 'One hundred and eighty'. The player is then shown lighting a cigarette. Imagine the furore if the tournament were being sponsored by the Mafia and the player were a heroin addict, shown injecting himself.

Why do we allow society to subject healthy young teenagers, youngsters whose lives are complete before they start smoking, to paying through the nose for the rest of their lives just for the privilege of destroying themselves mentally and physically in a lifetime of slavery, a lifetime of filth and disease?

You may feel that I over-dramatize the facts. Not so. My father was cut off in his early fifties because of cigarette smoking. He was a strong man and might still have been alive today.

I believe I was within an inch of dying during my forties, although my death would have been attributed to a brain haemorrhage rather than to cigarette smoking. I now spend my life being consulted by people who have been crippled by the disease or are in the last stages. And, if you care to think about it, you probably know of many too.

There is a wind of change in society. A snowball has started that I hope this book will help turn into an avalanche.

You can help too by spreading the message.

FINAL WARNING

You have joined the millions of other ex-smokers who thought that they could never get free but who have finally escaped from the slavery of nicotine addiction. Congratulations!

You can now enjoy the rest of your life as a happy non-smoker. In order to make sure that you do, you need to follow these simple instructions:

1 Keep this book safely in a place where you can easily refer to it. Do not lose it, lend it out or give it away.

2 If you ever start to envy another smoker, realize that they will be envious of you. You are not being deprived. They are.

3 Remember you did not enjoy being a smoker. That's why you stopped. You do enjoy being a non-smoker.

4 Never doubt your decision never to smoke again. You know it's the correct decision.

5 If you ever start thinking 'Shall I have a cigarette?' remember there is no such thing as 'one'. So the question you need to ask is not 'Shall I have a cigarette?' but 'Do I want to become a smoker again, all day every day, sticking those things into my mouth and setting light to them?' The answer:

'NO! THANK GOODNESS I'M FREE!'

You have achieved something really marvellous. Every time we hear of a smoker escaping from the sinking ship, we get a feeling of enormous satisfaction.

It would give us great pleasure to hear that you have freed yourself from the slavery of the weed. Please sign the letter and add your comments, and send it back to: Nancy Toth, 461 North Service Road, Unit 87, Oakville, Ontario, L6M 2VS

....

YIPPEE! I'M A NON-SMOKER

Signed .... Date ....

Name ....

Address ....

. ... Postcode ....

Comments ....

. ...

. ...

. ...

Thousands of smokers have become happy non-smokers easily and painlessly by attending one of Allen Carr's clinics where with a success rate of over 90% he guarantees that you'll find it easy to stop or your money back. All correspondence and enquiries about ALLEN CARR'S BOOKS, VIDEOS AND AUDIO TAPES should be addressed to your nearest clinic.

CANADIAN CLINIC

TORONTO:
461 North Service Road,
Unit B7, Oakville,
Ontario, L6M 2V5.
Tel: 905 827 3888.
Fax: 905 827 9434.
Therapist: Nancy Toth.
E-mail:aceasyway@msn.com

SOUTH AFRICAN CLINIC

CAPETOWN:
P.O. Box 5269, Helderberg,
Somerset West, 7135.
Tel: 083 600 5555.
Fax: 083 8 600 5555.
Therapist: Dr. Charles Nel.

USA CLINICS

TEXAS:
12823 Kingsbridge Lane,
Houston, Texas 77077.
Tel: 281 597 1904. Fax: 281 597 9829.
Therapist: Laura Cattell.
E-mail: ACatt38826@aol.com

NEW JERSEY:
Tel: 732 730 1850
or 1-800 524 9949.
Therapist: Keith Newmark.
E-mail:acezway@juno.com

ST LOUIS:
Tel: 1 800 524 9949.
Therapist: Keith Newmark.
E-mail: acezway@juno.com

ALLEN CARR U.K.
Website: http://www.qwerty.co.uk/allencarr

BIRMINGHAM: 415 Hagley Road West, Quinton, Birmingham B32 2AD.
Tel & Fax: 0121 423 1227. Therapist: Jason Vale. E-mail: JASEYBEAN@AOL.COM

BRISTOL: Unit 13, The Coach House, 2 Upper York Street, Bristol BS2 8QN.
Tel: 0117 908 1106. Therapist: John Emery.

DEVON: Angel Cottage, Cutteridge Farm, Whitestone, Exeter EX4 2HE.
Tel: 01392 811603. Therapist: Trevor Emdon. E-mail: trevor@emdon.freeserve.co.uk

EDINBURGH: 48 Eastfield, Joppa, Edinburgh, EH15 2PN.
Tel & Fax: 0131 660 6688. Therapist: Derek McGuff. E-mail: derek@djmcg.demon.co.uk

GLASGOW: Meadow House, Meadowmill, Tranent.
Tel: 01875 613384. Therapist: Joe Bergin.

KENT: Tel: 01622 679 595. Therapist: Angela Jouanneau.

LONDON: 1c Amity Grove, Raynes Park, London SW20 0LQ Tel & Fax: 0181 944 7761.
Therapist: John Dicey

NORTH EAST: 10 Dale Terrace, Dalton-le-Dale, Seaham, County Durham, SR7 8QP.
Tel & Fax: 0191 581 0449. Therapist: Tony Attrill.

SOUTH COAST: Christchurch Business Centre, Grange Road, Dorset BH23 4JD.
Tel: 01425 272757. Fax: 01425 274250. Therapist: Anne Emery. E-mail: AEmery3192@aol.com

SOUTHAMPTON: Tel: 01425 272757. Fax: 01425 274250. Therapist: Anne Emery.
E-mail: AEmery3192@aol.com

YORKSHIRE: 577 Harehills Lane, Leeds LS9 6NQ. Tel: 0700 900 0305.
Fax: 01904 340 159. Mobile: 0498 762 892. Therapist: Diana Evans.

ALLEN CARR AUSTRALIA

MELBOURNE: 148 Central Road, Nunawading, Vic 3131, Victoria.
Tel & Fax: 03 9894 8866. Therapist: Trudy Ward. E-mail: easywaya@bigpond.com
SYDNEY: 40 Ashbrookes Road, Mount White, NSW 2250.
Tel: 02 9328 2978. Therapist: John Ryff. E-mail: john_ryff@hotmail.com

ALLEN CARR AUSTRIA

Website: http://www.allen-carr.at

VIENNA: Tel: 01 333 1355. Fax: 08031 463068. Therapist: Erich Kellermann
E-mail: erich.kellermann@allen-carr.at
SALZBURG: Tel: 0662 878718. Fax: 08031 463068. Therapist: Erich Kellermann.
E-mail: erich.kellermann@allen-carr.at

ALLEN CARR BELGIUM

ANTWERP: Marialei 47, 2018 Antwerpen. Tel: 03 281 6255. Fax: 03 744 0608.
Therapist: Dirk Nielandt. E-mail: easyway@online.be

ALLEN CARR ECUADOR

QUITO: Veintimilla 878 y Amazonas, P.O. Box 17-03-179, Quito.
Tel & Fax: 02 56 33 44. Tel: 02 82 09 20. Therapist: Ingrid Wittich. E-mail: toisan@pi.pro.ec

ALLEN CARR FRANCE

MARSEILLE: 70 Rue St Ferreol, 13006 Marseille. Tel: 04 91 33 54 55.
Fax: 04 91 33 32 77. Therapist: Erick Serre. E-mail: ELYFRANCE@COMPUSERVE.COM
ALPES: Centre Allen Carr ALPES, BP 203, 73277 ALBERTVILLE Cedex
Tel: 04 79 37 76 02. Fax: 04 79 32 84 72. Therapist: Daniel Gille.
ROUSSILLON: 1 Rue Pierre Curie, 66000 Perpignan. Tel: 04 68 34 40 68.
Fax: 04 68 62 16 09. Therapist: Eugene Salas. E-mail: eugenesalas@minitel.net

ALLEN CARR GERMANY

Website: http://www.allen-carr.de E-mail: info@allen-carr.de

MUNICH: Hochgstattweg 8, 82216 Uberacker. Tel: 08135 8466.
Fax: 08135 8920. Therapists: Petra Wackerle & Stephan Kraus. E-mail: info@allen-carr.de
STUTTGART: Heumadener Str. 11, 70329 Stuttgart-Hedelfingen. Tel: 0711 4209154
Fax: 08135 8920. Therapists: Petra Wackerle & Stephan Kraus. E-mail: info@allen-carr.de
BAD SALZUFLEN: Im neuen Land 20a, 32107 Bad Salzuflen. Tel: 05222 797622.
Fax: 05222 797624. Therapist: Wolfgang Rinke. E-mail: wolfgang.rinke@allen-carr.de
DUSSELDORF: Steffenstr. 4, 40545 Duesseldorf. Tel: 0211 5571738.
Fax: 0211 5571740. Therapist: Axel Matheja. E-mail: axel.matheja@allen-carr.de
BERLIN: Tel: 030 21750488. Fax: 030 21750489. E-mail: info@allen-carr.de
HAMBURG: Tel: 040 28051056. Therapist: Regina Hildebrandt. E-mail: info@allen-carr.de
FRANKFURT: Tel: 06701 960673. Therapist. Elfi Blume. E-mail: elfi.blume@allen-carr.de

ALLEN CARR HOLLAND

AMSTERDAM: Pythagorasstraat 22, 1098 GC Amsterdam.
Tel: 020 465 4665. Fax: 020 465 6682. Therapist: Eveline De Mooij.

UTRECHT: De Beaufortlaan 22 B, 3768 MJ Soestduinen (gem. Soest).
Tel (stop smoking): 035 60 29458. Tel: (weight): 035 60 32153. Fax: 035 60 322 65.
Therapist: Nicolette de Boer.

ROTTERDAM: Mathenesserlaan 290, 3021 HV Rotterdam. Tel: 010 244 07 09.
Fax: 010 244 07 10. Therapist: Kitty van't Hof

ALLEN CARR HONG KONG

WANCHAI: Suite B, 19th Floor, LoYong Court Commercial Building, Wanchai.
Tel: 852 2893 1571. Fax: 852 2554 2958. Therapists: Jon Lewis-Evans & Leo Ngai.
E-mail: easyway@hkwww.com

ALLEN CARR ICELAND

REYKJAVIK: Ljosheimar 4, 104 Reykjavik. Tel: 354 553 9590. Fax: 354 588 7060.
Therapists: Petur Einarsson & Valgeir Skagfjord. E-mail: pein@ismennt.is

ALLEN CARR IRELAND

DUBLIN: 123 Coolamber Park, Templeogue, Dublin 16. Tel: 01 494 1644.
Tel & Fax: 01 493 9313. Therapist: Brenda Sweeney. E-mail: seansw@iol.ie

ALLEN CARR ISRAEL

JERUSALEM: P.O. Box 127, Givat Ze'ev. Tel: 02 624 2586. Therapist: Michael Goldman.

ALLEN CARR ITALY

MILAN: Studio Pavanello, Piazza Argentina 4, 20124 Milan. Tel: 02 29 52 9251.
Therapist: Francesca Cesati.

BOLOGNA: Via Porrettana, 449, 40037 Sasso Marconi (BO) Tel & Fax: 051 840675.
Therapist: Brian McDonald

ALLEN CARR SPAIN

MADRID: C/Fernandez De Los Rios, 106, 1. IZQ. 28015 Madrid.
Tel: 91 543 8504. Therapist: Geoffrey Molloy & Rhea Sivi. E-mail: sivimoll@arrakis.es

ALLEN CARR SWITZERLAND

Website: http://www.allen-carr.ch

ZURICH: Bernhofstr. 34, CH - 8134 Adliswil. Tel: 0041 1 7105678.
Fax: 0041 1 7105683. Therapist: Cyrill Argast. E-mail: cyrill.argast@allen-carr.ch